COMING TO CROSSROADS

The Harper & Row Design for Reading

Eldonna L. Evertts

Byron H. VanRoekel

HARPER & ROW, PUBLISHERS

New York   Evanston   San Francisco   London

1817

ACKNOWLEDGMENTS

Grateful acknowledgment is made to the following authors and publishers who granted permission to reprint these selections:

"Al and the Magic Lamp" by Benjamin Elkin. Copyright © 1963 by Benjamin Elkin. Published by Harper & Row, Publishers, Inc. Reprinted by permission of the author and publisher. "All Around Athlete" by Eldonna L. Evertts. "April Rain Song," from THE DREAM KEEPER by Langston Hughes. Copyright © 1932 by Alfred A. Knopf, Inc. Copyright renewed 1960 by Langston Hughes. Reprinted by permission of Alfred A. Knopf, Inc., New York. "Audubon: Wildlife Artist" by Byron H. VanRoekel.

"Barkham Street," Part one—"Edward," an adaptation of Chapter 1 of A DOG ON BARKHAM STREET by M. S. Stolz; copyright © 1960 by M. S. Stolz. Part two—"Martin," an adaptation of Chapter 2 of THE BULLY OF BARKHAM STREET by Mary Stolz; copyright © 1963 by Mary Stolz. Reprinted by permission of Harper & Row, Publishers, Inc., and Roslyn Targ Literary Agency, Inc., New York. "Bobby Bronto-saurus" by Barbara Beatty. "Brownstone," from STANYON STREET AND OTHER SORROWS by Rod McKuen. Copyright © 1954, 1960, 1961, 1962, 1963, 1964, 1965, 1966 by Rod McKuen. Reprinted by permission of Random House, Inc., New York, and Michael Joseph Ltd., London.

"The Canoe in the Rapids," from THE TALKING CAT by Natalie Savage Carlson. Copyright © 1952 by Natalie Savage Carlson. Reprinted by permission of Harper & Row, Publishers, Inc. "Carl Akeley" by Byron H. VanRoekel. "Cat on Couch" (first two lines) from LIGHT AND DARK by Barbara Howes. Copyright © 1955 by Barbara Howes. Reprinted by permission of Wesleyan University Press, Middletown, Connecticut. "Champions Don't Cry," an adaptation of Chapters 2, 17, and 18, and pages 187-198 of CHAMPIONS DON'T CRY by Nan Gilbert. Copyright © 1960 by Mildred Geiger Gilbertson. Published by Harper & Brothers. Adapted and reprinted by permission of the author and author's agent, Scott Meredith Literary Agency, Inc., New York. "The Cocks and the Eagle," an Aesop fable. "The Coin" by Sara Teasdale, from STARS TONIGHT by Sara Teasdale. Copyright © 1930 by Sara Teasdale Filsinger. Copyright renewed 1948 by Mamie T. Wheless. Reprinted by permission of The Macmillan Company, New York. "The Coins of Lin Foo," from LEGENDS IN ACTION—TEN PLAYS OF TEN LANDS by Nellie McCaslin. Copyright © 1963, 1945 by Harper & Row, Publishers, Incorporated. Reprinted by permission of Walter H. Baker Company, Boston. "Come to the Fair" by Byron H. VanRoekel.

"Daniel Hale Williams: Surgeon" by Eldonna L. Evertts. "David and Phoenix," an adaptation of pages 19-40 from DAVID AND THE PHOENIX by Edward Ormondroyd. Copyright © 1957 by Edward Ormondroyd. Reprinted by permission of Follett Publishing Company, Chicago.

"Edward Cliff: Conservationist" by Eldonna L. Evertts. "The Elixir of Long Life," from MORE FOLK TALES FROM CHINA by Lim Siantek. Copyright © 1948 by The John Day Company. Published by the John Day Company, New York. Reprinted by permission of the author and publisher.

"Flight" (first two lines) from THE LOST PILOT by James Tate. Copyright © 1967 by Yale University, New Haven, Connecticut. Reprinted by permission of Yale University Press. "The Future of Spaceship Earth" by Christine Winslow.

(continued on page 448)

Contents

*Indicates that a **word highlight** will be found at the end of these selections.

5

Unit One   Contests and Conquests

THE PERAMBULATIN' PUMPKIN

Down in Beaverdam Valley the mountain folk had gathered for the county fair. Mr. Zeke Calloway held up a pumpkin decorated with the blue ribbon for the first prize and grinned triumphantly at his neighbor, Mr. Hank Huggins.

"Reckon you don't grow pumpkins like that on your side of the mountain!" he crowed.

"Law me," drawled Hank who had been known on occasion to stretch the truth somewhat. "Law me, that little bitty thing would look like a peanut beside the pumpkins in my patch."

"Mighty funny thing you didn't bring any of your huge pumpkins to the fair," sniggered Zeke. "Mighty funny."

"Well, to tell the truth I was aiming to bring one but we had a little accident up at our place this morning. It broke up my plans somewhat."

"What kind of accident?" asked Zeke.

"Well, you see it was this way: my wife had laid off to bring a pumpkin pie to the fair. She was up early baking the crust. As soon as it was done, she climbed the mountain to the field where the pumpkins were a-growing among the cornstalks.

"Of course all the pumpkins were too big and too heavy to carry, so she set out to cut a slab out of one, enough to make the filling for her pie.

"Seems she had trouble with that, too. Those pumpkins were so thick through that her arm wasn't long enough to reach into the inside where the juicy part was. But she was bound to get some of the very best part for she meant to take first prize with her pie. So what did she do but hack out a big hole and climb through it right into the center of that pumpkin.

"Now that would have been all right if the field where I planted 'em hadn't been so steep. But you know how it is—sometimes a pumpkin will break off the vine by its own weight and go rolling down the mountain.

"Well, you can just picture what happened when that hefty wife of mine added her weight to the strain already on that vine. Before she knew what was happening she was tumbling head over heels inside that pumpkin as it rolled out of the cornfield.

"I was in the barn lot hitching up the mule to the wagon when I looked up and saw it coming, a-picking up speed every minute. Before I could gather my wits to think what to do, it had hit the lot fence with a crash that sent the rails flying like matches. It tore through the barnyard, hit my wagon broadside, and sent the wheels flying four ways at once. The chickens and ducks ran squawking for their lives.

"I could hear my old lady screeching, 'Oh, my pie! my pie!' as she went reeling on down the mountain inside that pumpkin.

"Well, sir, there wasn't a thing I could do about it, so I figured there wasn't any use to get excited. I went to the ledge and looked after it awhile as it went bumping and bounding down toward the valley, cutting through the underbrush as it went.

"About halfway down I saw it bounce across the highway and crash into a wagon loaded with apples. Folks in the valley told me afterwards that apples rained down on 'em thick as hail for half an hour or so. They thought a miracle had happened up in the sky. Soon after that I lost sight of the thing, so I went on back to the barn.

"One look at my wagon told me I wasn't going to haul any pumpkins to the fair, but I didn't see

any call to give up the trip. I could still go on muleback. The pumpkin had headed in that direction anyhow, and I thought I might as well jog down and see what had happened to my wife.

"Into the cabin I went and put on my store-bought Sunday clothes. As I was on my way out again, my eyes lit on a pie crust sitting there on the kitchen table. It was nice and brown and crisp-looking and it came to me that this must have been what my wife was a-screeching about as she went rolling down the mountain. I picked it up, wrapped it carefully so it wouldn't break, and put it into my saddlebag.

"Then I straddled my mule and started on down the trail, wondering as I jogged along where my old lady could have ended up.

"When I got down to Beaverdam I began to get a suspicion that she had rolled right onto the fairground. There was a hole in the side of the fence that would have let an elephant through, and the trail of wreckage inside the grounds looked like a hurricane had torn through. Folks were running around like ants trying to fix up the damage.

"I followed the trail of ruin and at the end of it, sure enough, there sat my wife in the wreckage of the pumpkin. It had smashed against a stone chimney.

" 'Oh my pie, my pie! Now I've got no pie to take to the fair,' she was still a-wailing.

" 'Why, Honey, you have,' I said to her as I rode up. I put my hand into my saddlebag and brought out the pie crust.

" 'But—but Hank,' she said. 'A pumpkin pie's got to have sugar and eggs and spices and I don't know what-all.'

" 'Not this pumpkin, Honey,' I said to her. 'The pumpkins I raise are flavored already. You just scoop out one of these pieces and spread it in the crust "as is," and you'll have a finer, tastier pie than anybody at the fair.'

"Well, sir, she got up from there, brushed herself off, straightened her hair a little, and fixed up that pie just as I told her to. You can see for yourself what the upshot was.

"Look over there now, across that table full of wild strawberry jam beside that fancy patchwork quilt hanging on the wall. There she stands. See that pie she's a-holding? That's the very pie and if it hasn't got a blue ribbon a-hanging on it I'll eat my Sunday pants."

"Well, Hank," said Mr. Zeke Calloway, "all I've got to say is, it's too bad they're not offering prizes for tall tales. If they were there'd be two blue ribbons in your family."

When All Else Fails...

If you encountered the word *stringent* out of context, that is, not used in a meaningful sentence, you would have no *clues* to its meaning. It has no familiar root and no familiar prefix or suffix such as *un-*, *-ment*, or *-ly* to help you. It is not a compound made up of known words. When you cannot use this method of finding the meaning of a word and *stringent* appears out of context, you would have to look it up in a dictionary.

However, if *stringent* appeared in context, you would have *clues* to its meaning. For example, "Jan heard that the rules at the swimming pool were stringent." The clue is *rules*. From the context of this sentence would you know what is being said about the rules? Are they strict, lax, or just right?

Further reading may give more information. "With such a list of 'don'ts' to follow, she wondered how anyone could have fun." Does this sentence help make the meaning of *stringent* clear?

What do the above paragraphs tell you about attacking unfamiliar words in context? Would you have wasted valuable reading time by checking in the dictionary too soon? Using the title of this page, can you make a rule for using the dictionary to find word meanings?

"COME TO THE FAIR!"

This cry has always brought excitement to the hearts of young and old. It means that the time has come for people to assemble so they can look at exhibits, trade their goods and livestock, participate in contests, and just have fun.

Ever since people began to cultivate the land and tame animals, fairs have been popular events. After the autumn harvest, tribesmen would often hold celebrations in thanksgiving for a good year.

Eventually, fairs were held for the purpose of carrying on peaceful trade. Although the tribesmen were often at war with men of other tribes, they declared a truce at the "fair ground." The people regarded this place as holy and believed that the gods would punish anyone who fought or cheated there.

Gradually, villages became larger and cities were built. Since the city inhabitants lived so close together, it was easy for them to meet for religious holidays, which were occasions for honoring the gods. After the festival, fairs were held at which they sold their wares. The original Olympic games were held at one such Greek fair.

By the Middle Ages, fairs were common in many parts of the world.

The oldest fair in Ireland was held at a burial ground. The fair began in the middle of July each year and continued until late August. Outstanding athletes competed in horseback riding, running, jumping, and spear-throwing.

It was at the fairs of Germany where such amusements as acrobatics, fire-eating, and tightrope dancing were perfected.

In England, as in Ireland, the early fairs were held at burial grounds. A special court called the "Pie Powder Court" was set up at the fair to try those who broke the law. The strange title came from the French words *pied poudreux*, meaning "dusty foot." This name was given to merchants because they got dusty and dirty from traveling.

During the 1200's the city of Kinsai was the center of trade in China. Half a million customers came to these fairs that were held every third day. The festivities took place in ten huge squares, each four miles apart. Each square had a great palace where officials settled arguments about trade. Five and a half tons of pepper, which was a highly prized spice of the time, were sold every day.

Perhaps because the fairs were connected with religious events, the customers and performers were honest and orderly. However, in the seventeenth century, England held the first great fair that put amusement above everything else. As a result, the crowds were loud and disorderly and the old, strict rules of honesty were broken by much fighting, stealing, and crookedness.

Before the discovery of the Americas, the Aztecs of Mexico held weekly fairs in honor of their gods. Huge crowds also gathered for trading. For money they used bits of tin, scoops of cocoa, and quills filled with gold dust. When the Spaniards first came to Mexico after the discovery of the Americas and saw this fair, they were amazed by its size, cleanliness, and orderliness.

After the Spanish conquest, a fair was established in Panama. This was the only place where Spanish-Americans were permitted to sell goods.

Early fairs in the United States were held mainly in farming communities. In 1810 an agricultural organization put on the Berkshire Cattle Show. But prizes were given for many other products besides livestock. For the first time, women took an active part in fairs. They entered tastily prepared foods and handmade household goods in contests.

Children participated in contests that were much like those of their parents. There were livestock shows for boys, and cooking contests and sewing bees for girls.

A favorite contest enjoyed by both men and boys involved turning a greased pig loose in a pen. The contestants would try to catch the pig and carry it across a goal line. It was quite a challenge to hold onto an armful of squealing, squirming, greased pig!

One of the main reasons for holding a local or county fair was education. People gathered to exchange ideas about farming methods, livestock rearing, and homemaking. Many contests were held in which people showed skills they used in their everyday lives such as log-chopping and cow-milking. But a fair was also a time to meet old friends and have a good time.

Local and county agricultural fairs developed into our regional agricultural and industrial fairs. In some places today, big state fairs are held once a year. Another type of fair today is an exposition, which features industrial, commercial, and scientific developments. One country or many countries may display inventions or products, or give information on services. Expositions on a large scale are usually called *World's Fairs*.

The first World's Fair was held in London in 1851. It was called "The Exposition of the Industry of all Nations." This exposition attracted over six million visitors during the five and a half months it ran. Forty nations exhibited their art and inventions, including the McCormick reaper and the Colt automatic pistol, both made in the United States.

In each World's Fair that followed, exciting new inventions and discoveries were brought to the attention of the visitors. The directors of the "World's Columbian Exposition," held in 1893, wanted something different—something the world had never seen. A young engineer named Ferris had a clever idea and fair-goers have been riding Ferris wheels ever since!

The 1915 "Panama-Pacific International Exposition" held in San Francisco was planned to highlight art and beauty, not industry and invention. The planners turned the San Francisco fairgrounds into a fairyland of lights and beautiful buildings!

The World's Fairs of today are filled with wonders of the Space Age. Industries from all over the world spend millions of dollars to give visitors a look at the twenty-first century.

As man's way of life and the world in which he lives have changed, fairs have grown larger and have become more exciting. People travel vast distances to attend them. What do you suppose the fairs of the future will be like? Perhaps your grandchildren will attend the first "Exposition of the Way of Life of all Planets"—held on the fairground of the Solar System, Earth's Moon!

---

1. How did the character of fairs change from prehistoric fairs to the fairs of the Middle Ages?

2. Why do you suppose that pepper was such a highly prized spice?

3. How does a world fair differ from a county fair?

4. Do you agree with the author's forecast for the future of fairs? Why or why not?

The French word for "count" means "companion to the king." Each *conte* governed a tract of land. When *conte* was adopted into English, it came to mean "a subdivision of a state." **County** still looks and sounds like the French from which it came.

THE COCKS AND THE EAGLE

"I'm the champion! I'm the champion!" the cock crowed as he strutted proudly about the barnyard.

In a dark corner beside the barn lay the young cock whom he had just beaten in a fierce battle. The proud crowing of the older cock was even more painful to the loser than the cuts he had received in the fight.

The winner continued to strut and boast in front of all the animals in the barnyard. Not satisfied that everyone could see and hear him, the champion flew to the roof of the barn where he crowed and bragged louder than ever.

Suddenly a huge eagle swooped down from the sky, snatched the surprised cock from the roof, and carried him away. Very shortly, the cock became the eagle's dinner.

In the meantime, the young cock who had been defeated came out from his hiding place to become king of the barnyard.

So, you see: Pride comes before a downfall.

ALL-AROUND ATHLETE

Outside the huge stadium a cab screeched to a halt. A girl jumped out, pushed her way through the crowd, and dashed into the locker room. Moments later, as she took her place on the field among the other girls, the loudspeaker blared.

"Welcome to the 1932 National Track and Field Championship Meet!"

As the announcer began calling the names of the teams that would be competing, the newcomer looked around her. *There must be two hundred girls here*, she thought. *That's a lot of competition!* But Mildred "Babe" Didrikson was glad to be a part of it. She knew the winners would be given places on the United States Olympic team, and that had been her goal for a long time.

"Illinois Women's Athletic Club," the announcer called out. Twenty-two girls ran onto the track.

Babe ran her hand through her ruffled hair. "Wow!" she whispered to the girl next to her, "That's a lot of team!"

"Where's the rest of yours?" the girl asked.

"I'm it," Babe answered.

"Do you mean you're going to try to compete all alone?" The girl looked at Babe in astonishment.

"Not going to TRY," determination showed in Babe's face, "going to DO! I'll win, too. I didn't come all the way from Texas to Illinois just to lose."

"You sound pretty sure of yourself, Texas." The girl grinned wryly and turned away.

Babe frowned. *Of course I am. Why should the girl look offended? I only said what was true. If I know I'm going to win, I always say so. That's only honest.*

"Employers Casualty!" The loudspeaker interrupted her thoughts.

"Here goes," Babe said under her breath. She squared her shoulders and ran onto the track waving her arms wildly at the crowd. For a minute there was silence. Then the surprised crowd burst into cheers and clapped loudly for the lone girl.

They were cheering her courage more than anything else, and she knew it. Next to the other husky girls, her own skinny body looked frail and weak.

I'll have to show those nice people a thing or two, she thought.

Once the competition began Babe realized that she had a difficult task ahead of her. Of the ten events, she was entered in eight. The other girls were participating in only one or two because of their large teams. There would be a chance for them to rest. But Babe knew she was in peak condition. It was one of those days when she felt as if she could do anything!

Her first four events involved running and jumping. First she competed in the hurdle race. This was followed by the high jump and the broad jump. She placed well in these but was not as successful in the 100-yard dash. She had not expected to be. Straight running had never been her specialty.

She didn't expect to do well in either the discus throw or the shot-put. She hadn't practiced very much for these. Besides, the other girls looked stronger. But in the discus throw she won fourth place, and in the shot-put she placed first!

In the last two throwing events she was confident of her ability. Why, she'd been playing baseball ever since she was a child! In fact, that's how she'd earned her nickname. Her friends had said she could throw as well as Babe Ruth. So she was not really surprised when she won the baseball throw. And she already held the world's record in the javelin toss. In this last event, she beat her own record!

At the end of the meet she ran off the field, tired but happy. The results of the competition were announced over the loudspeaker.

"In second place with twenty-two points, the team from the Illinois Women's Athletic Club. And the winner—with a total of thirty points—the one-girl team from Texas, Mildred "Babe" Didrikson of Employers Casualty!"

She'd done it! She'd won the meet by herself!

After dinner Babe picked up a newspaper. The story was there. Reporters called her a "Wonder Girl" and a "Super Athlete." They said her performance had been the most amazing in track and field history! She had placed in seven of the eight events she had entered, winning five and tying for first in a sixth. She had certainly won her place on the Olympic team!

The newspaper fell to her lap and her thoughts drifted back through the years.

Even in grade school she knew what she wanted to be when she grew up—the greatest woman athlete who ever lived. Her father encouraged her interest in sports. When Babe was very young, he told her about the news on the sports page of the paper. When she learned to read well enough, she studied the columns herself.

In the summer of 1928 the papers were full of stories about the Olympic Games. Babe was only fourteen years old that year when she announced, "Papa, I'm going to be in the Olympics next year."

"I'm afraid you'll have to wait," her father smiled.

"But why, Papa?"

"Because the Olympics are held only every four years."

Right then she decided to begin training.

Along the block where Babe lived were seven hedges. Each day she jumped over them, but there was one that bothered her. It was taller than the others and she couldn't clear it. One day she asked the owner if he would trim the hedge to match the others on the block. He agreed!

In the late 1920's one of the most popular sports for women was basketball. Babe learned to play the game well. One day a man from Employers Casualty Insurance Company watched her play. He was impressed with her ability and asked her to join the company's team. He also offered her a job working in the office. Babe accepted both. For the next three years she was an All-American basketball player.

In the summer of 1929 she watched her first track meet. She especially liked the hurdle events, for she was reminded of her hedge-jumping days. The throwing events also appealed to her.

Shortly after the track meet, the insurance company decided to organize a track team so the girls would have something to do in their spare time during the summer months. Babe signed up for the team. Every day after dinner she practiced running and jumping. Later in competition she won several championships.

One day she was asked if she would represent Employers Casualty in the National Championship Meet. Here was her chance to qualify for the Olympics! Of course her answer was "Yes!"

The paper slipped out of her lap and rattled to the floor, bringing Babe's attention back to the present. Today her dreams had come true. She had won! *It's time to celebrate*, she thought.

That night she went dancing with some friends. She wasn't even tired!

Next morning Babe was up early for a workout. Then on the way back to Texas, she exercised in the aisle of the train. This was no time to let up on training. The real test—the Olympics—lay ahead.

During the rest of her short life Babe won many honors. After the 1932 Olympics, reporters voted her the Woman Athlete of the Year. Then in 1950 she was voted the greatest woman athlete of the first half of the twentieth century.

Babe excelled in every sport in which she participated. But throughout her life the achievement she remembered best was the track meet she won all alone.

---

1. How old was Babe when this National Track and Field Championship Meet took place?

2. How did Employers Casualty help Babe toward her goal of the Olympics? Has anyone ever helped you meet some goal? In what way?

3. In what ways was Babe an "all-around athlete"?

4. Why is good physical condition so important for athletes? Why is good physical condition important for you?

Pause to Think

Kerry Smith's beagle raced down the street.
Kerry, Smith's beagle, raced down the street.

How are the above sentences alike? How do they differ?

When speaking, a person helps to convey meaning with stress for emphasis, sentence contour (for example, raising and lowering the voice), and phrasing (grouping of words). In translating the spoken sentence into a written one, how does the writer indicate these things? Read the sentences at the top of this page aloud, then discuss how stress, contour, and phrasing alter the meaning in the second sentence.

What is missing in the following sentence? *Bruce had a cold sore throat pains and fever.* Do you know whether Bruce had a cold or a cold sore? Why not? Read this sentence aloud, giving it two different meanings.

Jerry just returned from the store. *He bought chicken soup ice cream sandwich bread cinnamon buns corn oil coffee cream.* Do you know what he bought? Why not? Using commas, rewrite the italicized sentence in three different ways without changing the word order so that it will have different meanings. Read your sentences aloud. Discuss how commas altered the meaning of each sentence.

KING MIDAS'S[1] EARS

"King Midas's Ears" is a Greek myth. A myth is a story which attempts to explain some aspect of nature.

One day King Midas (the same King Midas who one day foolishly wished that everything he touched would turn to gold) agreed to judge a music contest between the woodland god Pan and Apollo, god of the sun and prophecy.

Midas didn't know the meaning of the word *trouble* until that fateful day.

[1] Although the story of King Midas's ears is a legend, King Midas himself is not a legendary character. He really lived about 700 B.C. in a country which is now a part of Turkey.

King Midas really should have known better than to agree to judge a music contest. What ear did he have for music? Besides, both of the contestants were gods—and they had most unpleasant ways of punishing those who displeased them. Nevertheless, good-natured King Midas was pleased when his friend, the woodland god Pan,[2] asked him to judge a contest between himself and Apollo.[3]

Now Pan could play very well on his pipes of reed, and the nymphs and other woodland creatures loved to dance and sing to his gay tunes. But when Apollo played his lyre, the melody was so beautiful that even the breezes stopped in order to listen.

The mountain god, the other judge of the contest, unhesitatingly chose Apollo as the winner, but King Midas loudly insisted that he personally liked the music of Pan.

Apollo, god though he was, proved to be a poor loser. Turning to King Midas in anger he said, "Your ears are as deaf to good music as a donkey's. I'll make them the proper shape and size for one so stupid."

[2] The Greek god of the forests and meadows. He was half man and half goat, with the head, neck, and upper body of a man and the legs and feet of a goat.

[3] One of the great gods of Greek mythology. He was the god of light and purity and could foretell the future. He was especially skilled in music, poetry, and hunting.

Immediately Midas felt a strange tingling about his head. Grabbing his ears in horror, he found that they had become long, hairy, and movable. One look at himself in a quiet pond sent the poor king home by the darkest routes, wailing dismally at every step.

How his people would laugh if they knew! Well, he could see to it that they never found out. Hastily he made some caps to fit neatly over his head and hide his ears. Everyone in his kingdom immediately made little caps for themselves, thinking that the king was trying to start a new kind of headdress.[4]

Midas was forced to let just one person in on the secret, and that was his barber. He swore the man to silence, threatening him with a spine-tingling list of punishments if he dared to disobey.

What a burden for the poor barber! Here he was with the choicest bit of news in the entire kingdom but he could share it with no one, not even his wife. Day by day the urge to tell grew more powerful until he felt he had to disclose the secret to someone or burst.

But those punishments the king had described!

One night the barber could stand it no longer. He crept from his bed, raced out to the center of a

[4] Recently a statue of Midas with donkey ears hanging from beneath his cap was found in Turkey by archeologists.

large field, dug a hole in the ground, cupped his hands around his mouth and whispered, "King Midas has donkey ears!" He said it again and again and again until it was all out of his system. At last, feeling much better, he carefully replaced the dirt in the hole, patted it down firmly, and went home.

Summer came and the fields took on a cover of soft green. And then an odd thing happened. People passing a particular meadow near the king's palace began to hear sounds coming from a tall clump of reeds which had recently sprung up in the center of the field. They came close to listen and to their amazement heard the reeds, stirred gently by the breezes, whisper the words, "King Midas has donkey ears; King Midas has donkey ears . . ."

And the reeds have been chanting the story ever since, each time the breezes pass through them.

According to Greek mythology, one of the most terrible things in the world was the sight of the god Pan. He delighted in frightening people and made strange noises to terrorize those who dared enter his forests. From Pan comes the word **panic**.

OPEN ROAD TO EAGLE

It was warm for September. The only signs of fall were the leaves that were starting to drop. They were brown and dry, shriveled like old cocoons, and they crunched underfoot as Jack Pepper walked slowly down the street. He was average size for his eleven years; straight hair a medium brown, eyes the same color. Now and then he stopped his stroll, took aim, and kicked at a leaf as if it were a ball.

The midafternoon sun was still shining brightly, and its heat on his shoulders reminded Jack of the beach. *Turn right at the next corner, two blocks east to the dunes.* But now that school had started, he might just as well be living a thousand miles inland.

If only I could be at the beach! he thought. No problems there. He could lie on the soft sand, feeling its grittiness between his toes, listening to the sound of the ocean as he looked into the sky. It was just what the doctor had ordered—and the doctor had been giving orders to one Jack Pepper for nearly two years now.

Ever since he had come down with rheumatic fever, Jack had been listening to Dr. Shell.

"Take it easy, Jack," Dr. Shell told him.

"Be patient," Dr. Shell said.

"You're young and strong," the doctor assured him. "I'm sure that your heart murmur will clear up, if you give yourself a chance."

Ever since those weeks of endless care and rest, when Jack's joints were swollen and painful, Dr. Shell had kept repeating: "In a couple of years, you'll be able to do everything. Just be patient, boy."

Sure, Dr. Shell could be patient. Dr. Shell had forgotten how long "a few years" could be when the outdoors was calling. "Always remember the heart." How could Jack Pepper ever forget?

Jack walked a little more slowly, not eager to get where he was headed. Kids from school would be there, and Jack had stopped hanging around with them long, long ago. That way, he didn't have to hear about their baseball and their football and their surfing—all the things he could not be a part of. By now Jack was accustomed to walking alone, and thinking alone. He had grown almost comfortable in his own world apart. It was like the beach. No problems.

Now a problem *did* loom ahead of him, in the house with the shingles weathered gray by the salt air; there, on the corner, facing Ocean Avenue. Rick Frazer's house—Rick Frazer, patrol leader. But Jack Pepper? With the heart murmur? On his way to a Boy Scout meeting? *Why, really?*

"Boy Scouts," he muttered to himself. His mother and his doctor had come up with this crazy idea. "I think it would be good for him," Dr. Shell had said.

Jack was already late for the patrol meeting, of that he was sure. When he walked into the Frazers' recreation room, where the Rattlesnake Patrol was gathered for its first meeting, he sensed that all heads immediately turned, the better to see him. The talk stopped, and Jack wished he could disappear. *Vanish, somehow.* But even as the thought came to him, Rick Frazer was shaking his hand, saying, "Hi, grab yourself a seat," and Jack made straight for the nearest empty chair.

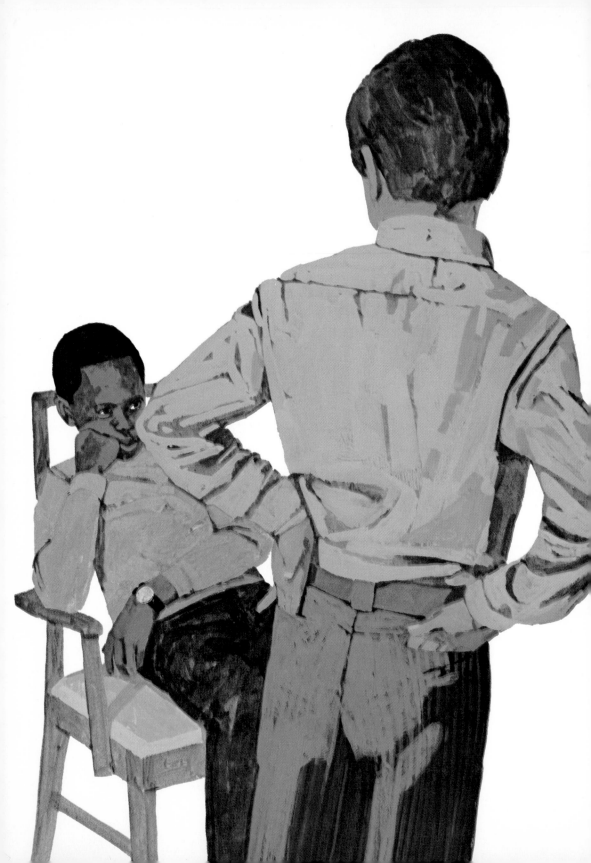

He looked around the room and saw that there were other new members of the Rattlesnakes who did not have uniforms. They, too, seemed uncomfortable, but then Jack remembered: There was one big difference between them and him. Once they got over the strangeness of this first meeting, they could jump in, go on past Tenderfoot . . . Second Class . . . First Class . . . even to Eagle. No barriers. For them the road was open all the way.

The thought stayed with him as he listened to Rick talk about the things ahead for the Scouts of Troop 2 and for the Rattlesnake Patrol—pretty much what Mr. Johnson, the Scoutmaster, had talked about at the troop meeting last week at school. Jack had listened attentively to the tall Negro scientist. Hikes. Camping. First Aid. The troop's Good Turn: planting dune grass to fight erosion. *Great for the other kids, but hardly for Jack Pepper.*

Now, in the Frazers' rec room, he let his gaze wander, not really focusing on anything or anybody. Then he noticed Stuart Parker, the only black in the patrol, slouched in his chair, looking fixedly at the floor. He must have felt Jack's gaze upon him, for he raised his eyes and returned a look so cold that Jack turned away and pretended to concentrate on his Scout handbook.

Jack found it hard to believe: the difference between Stuart at school and Stuart at Scouts. Stuart was in Jack's homeroom, the best athlete in the entire school. A pitcher, he had led the Little League in strikeouts the summer just past, and his batting was so good—over .400—he had saved many games as a pinch hitter. It seemed that whatever Stuart did, he did well—his ability matched by his enthusiasm and hustle. Eager, that was Stuart.

Jack frowned. Stuart Parker angry? Not part of any team? It didn't figure.

Walking home, Jack thought of the handbook stuck under his arm. He knew he would have to go back for the next patrol meeting and the meeting after that; his mother and his father and Dr. Shell, too, would see to it. They could convince him he should go, for a while, at least, but they couldn't fool him. Oh, sure, he could tag along . . . follow the other boys, without having to meet physical challenges. He knew he could even go to Eagle Scout by passing alternative tests. *But I will never really belong*, he thought. *Ever.*

Jack dutifully memorized the Scout Oath and Law . . . learned about the Outdoor Code and how to display the flag. The knot-tying came easy. *I am trying*, he told himself. *For what?* The longer he stayed with the Scouts, the more he would have to

sit by and listen to the others talk about things he couldn't be a part of.

After the next troop meeting, Jack was hoping to make a quick escape, when he was cornered by the Scoutmaster.

"How you doing, Jack?" Mr. Johnson smiled. "You'll be a Tenderfoot before you know it."

"Guess so . . . Yeah, it's great . . ."

That was what Mr. Johnson wanted to hear, wasn't it? Better to nod and smile than shout, "Look, I'm not like the others. I don't even care about being a Tenderfoot. So I do make Tenderfoot, where do I go after that?"

At least Mr. Johnson seemed pleased for the time being.

"Starting to rain outside, did you know?" the Scoutmaster said. "Coming down pretty hard, too. Finish scooping up your gear and I'll drive you home."

Jack wanted to say "No," and was annoyed with himself for being caught off base, without a ready excuse with which to decline Mr. Johnson's offer. On the other hand, perhaps, alone with the Scoutmaster, he could summon the courage to tell him he would not be coming back. But his annoyance returned when he found that Rick Frazer and Stuart Parker were already in Mr. Johnson's car, sitting in the backseat.

Mr. Johnson had been right. The rain was falling hard, windblown in sheets that curtained their view of the night. Stuart was the first to be dropped off; even though the porch light was on, the rain was so heavy that he was barely visible from the car as he went into his house. The streets were slick with wet leaves, and Mr. Johnson drove slowly. When he next stopped the car, Jack at first did not realize that it was in front of his house. He had been hoping that Mr. Johnson would be going by way of the Frazers'.

Now Jack was eager to get out of the car, and he quickly mumbled, "So long, and thanks very much for the ride," but Mr. Johnson stopped him as he was getting out.

"Rick and I need your help, Jack," Scoutmaster Johnson told him quietly.

"My help?"

"It's Stuart. He's not getting those knots right, and we're afraid he won't get his Tenderfoot badge along with the rest of you."

Big deal, thought Jack. *I should be concerned about Stuart Parker—Stuart, who can do just about everything?*

"No one else has learned his knots as fast as you have, Jack," Mr. Johnson went on. "We were wondering. Maybe you could work with Stuart at the next patrol meeting."

45

Jack shrugged. "Well, maybe," he said. "Anyway, so long."

During the next days Jack tried to tell his mother that he would not be going back to the Scout meetings, but the time never seemed right. Now it was

Wednesday—the day of the Rattlesnakes' meeting—
and getting on to the time he should be leaving for
the Frazers' house. Jack walked slowly from his room
and headed for the kitchen. He was not looking
forward to explaining his decision to his mother.

The doorbell rang, and Jack went rushing to
answer it, grateful for the interruption.

"Hi," said Mr. Johnson cheerfully. "I took off
from the lab a bit early to give you guys a hand at
the patrol meeting. Stopped on my way to pick up
Stuart, and I hope I can give you a lift, too. I
thought the two of you could work on those knots."

The words, "I'm not coming," stuck in Jack's
throat, and he found he couldn't say them—not with
Stuart already in the car. *Oh well*, he thought. *I'll
go. Then I'll tell them I'm not coming back.*

Later, in the Frazers' recreation room, the two
boys worked together tying knots. The clove hitch,
the sheet bend, the bowline—they tried them all.

"Not too tight," Jack cautioned. "No. The loop
goes like this. Don't be so nervous."

For Jack had discovered Stuart's problem: He was
trying too hard. He wanted so much to tie the knots
right that he couldn't. Simple as that. But, little by
little as Jack coached him, Stuart's fingers seemed to
find it easier to do the knots, and, at length, Jack
said, "Go ahead, Stuart, try it yourself now. Go

on!" And Stuart did, one knot after another, and each one right.

Suddenly Jack felt an excitement he had seldom before felt about anything. And when Stuart held up a perfect bowline, Jack was jubilant. "C'mon over after school tomorrow and we'll practice some more," he said.

Stuart walked home with Jack after school the next day, and together the boys worked on knots until it was almost suppertime. In between knots there seemed to be more and more to talk about.

While he did not say anything about leaving, Jack did tell Stuart that joining the Scouts was not his idea at all; it was what his mother and his doctor wanted him to do. And Stuart, too, began to open up, explaining that he wanted to become a Boy Scout because of Mr. Johnson.

"Mr. Johnson?" exclaimed Jack. "Our Scout-master?"

"You know what he does, don't you?"

"Sure," Jack said. "Of course. Everybody does. He works in the marine biological lab."

"He's the top guy there, that's all," Stuart said. "Met him last year, down at the beach the morning after Hurricane Eva. I was looking for shells. He saw my shovel and my dip net and my bucket, so he came over and we got to talking. He's been helping me with my collection ever since."

Stuart picked up some twine, looped it at the end of a length of rope, then began to wrap it tight. He scarcely looked at what he was doing.

"It was his idea that I go out for Scouts, and I . . ."

He stopped suddenly, yanked hard at the ends of the twine.

"I didn't want to, not at all, really. OK, so I know the other guys want me at school and in Little League, because I can help them win. But the Scouts? Don't see why they need me."

The question startled Jack into momentary silence, for, working with Stuart, he had forgotten that there were any differences between them—the one a boy with black skin, the other a boy with white; the one a healthy athlete, the other handicapped.

And now new thoughts came rushing in: *Someone else in the Rattlesnake Patrol felt that he was different from everyone else there. Someone else had a problem to solve.*

"Why wouldn't the Scouts want *you*?" Jack Pepper shook his head. "Honestly, Stuart, of all the dumb questions."

When he walked Stuart to the door, Jack suggested that they get together again the next afternoon.

"No, wait, wait, I've got a better idea," he said. "If the weather stays nice, maybe we could go to the beach right after school. It won't be a school night."

Jack thought the horizon looked unusually near as he sat on the sand and looked out over the ocean on the clear Indian summer afternoon of the next day. Farther down the beach, his trousers rolled to his knees, Stuart was wading in the still-warm water to hunt for shells left by the receding tide. Jack had been surprised to hear himself suggest to Stuart that they go together to the beach. Before, it was his sanctuary, where sun and sand asked nothing of him. Now he was able to share it.

Stuart was approaching now, carrying a bucketful of shells, and the two boys put back on their shoes and socks. "Knots, after supper," Jack reminded Stuart as they walked across the dunes. "Blindfolded this time."

And that, thought Jack, was really the least he could do before leaving the Scouts: see Stuart through his knots. Then Stuart wouldn't need him anymore—and it would be good-bye to the Rattlesnakes.

Stuart, too, was thinking ahead. "Do you realize we're going on our first hike two weeks from tomorrow?" he asked. "If we all make Tenderfoot."

"Don't count on me," said Jack.

"You're kidding," Stuart replied, and when Jack turned to look at him, he saw in Stuart's eyes the same cold look that had shocked him so at the first patrol meeting. Suddenly Jack realized he had shut himself so tightly in his own world that he had very nearly shut out a friend—and a chance to do all the things his doctor and his parents and his Scoutmaster knew he would someday be able to do.

"Let's hope I'm only kidding," Jack said. "I've got a hunch Dr. Shell will say OK, though. He promised I could do more as time goes on. This would be a good way to start."

 In the 1849 gold rush, some men didn't wear proper shoes for walking in the rough country around the gold fields. As a result, they suffered from tender feet. Since that time, anyone new and inexperienced has been called a **tenderfoot.**

To James

Do you remember
How you won
That last race...?
How you flung your body
At the start...
How your spikes
Ripped the cinders
In the stretch...
How you catapulted
Through the tape...
Do you remember...?
Don't you think
I lurched with you
Out of those starting holes...?
Don't you think
My sinews tightened
At those first
Few strides...
And when you flew into the stretch
Was not all my thrill
Of a thousand races
In your blood...?
At your final drive
Through the finish line
Did not my shout

Tell of the
Triumphant ecstasy
of victory . . . ?
Live
As I have taught you
To run, Boy—
It's a short dash
Dig your starting holes
Deep and firm
Lurch out of them
Into the straightaway
With all the power
That is in you
Look straight ahead
To the finish line
Think only of the goal
Run straight
Run high
Run hard
Save nothing
And finish
With an ecstatic burst
That carries you
Hurtling
Through the tape
To victory . . .

Interpreting Feelings and Emotions

Writers frequently tell their readers how characters feel by describing their actions and reactions and by painting word pictures of a scene. Read each of the descriptions below. From the list at the bottom of the page, choose the word or words which best describe how the character feels. Discuss in class the clues which helped you choose the words you did.

1. When Sue opened her report card, she could hardly believe her eyes. As soon as school was dismissed, she raced down the sidewalk toward home.

2. Kim stood on the porch and peered into the eerie blackness of the approaching storm. The trees groaned and creaked in the wind. Suddenly something crashed onto the roof. Kim dived for the screen door and crashed into the house.

3. Jeff shook the mysterious package once more. It was heavy but it didn't rattle or thump. He set it on the table and scratched his head. Maybe his father was playing a joke on him.

4. Karl shifted his weight. He had been waiting in the ticket line for ten minutes. He buttoned and unbuttoned his sweater, fidgeted with his watch, and even counted the change in his pocket.

amazed	frightened	puzzled	excited
proud	impatient	worried	curious

CHAMPIONS DON'T CRY

As far back as Sally's discovery that tennis was a real game, not just batting a ball against the house, she had dreamed of being a champion.

People admired champions, stared at them with respect, pointed them out. "That's Sally Barrett," they'd say. "You know—the tennis champion."

It was the afternoon following the Fairfield tournament, and not a bit too soon to start practicing seriously for the district meet in Maryville. Besides, perfect tennis weather lasted far too short a time to waste a single moment of it.

Sally caught up her racket and balls from the hall closet and ran out on the front porch, where Dennis lay comfortably in the swing.

"Denny," Sally begged, "let's play tennis, huh?"

The swing swayed back and forth. Dennis acted like a boy gone deaf.

"Denny," Sally begged again, "WILL you play tennis with me?" She poked the swing with her racket to upset its calm motion.

"Nope."

"Dennis Barrett! Why not? You've got your tennis shoes on."

"Gonna play with the guys."

"I can give you a better game than any of them, Denny. You KNOW I can."

"Look who's talking!"

"Well, I can! I guess I won a cup yesterday, didn't I? I guess that makes me—well, ALMOST a champion."

"Almost off your rocker, you mean."

"Look here, Dennis Barrett, Mr. Cochran says—"

"Oh, for Pete's sake, Mr. Cochran says, Mr. Cochran says! All he ever said was you've got pretty good strokes."

"Well, isn't that enough? If I've got the strokes, what else do I need?"

"Go away," Dennis begged, rolling over with his back to her. "Children don't interest me."

Sally aimed her racket for a deadly whack at him, but stopped. It was her only racket, and no longer new. The strings were frayed. If they hadn't loosened so much, they would surely have popped by now under some of the mighty drives Sally poured across the net.

Sally had some reason to hope of being a champion. When she practiced at the courts, passers-by stopped and stared in amazement. Sally,

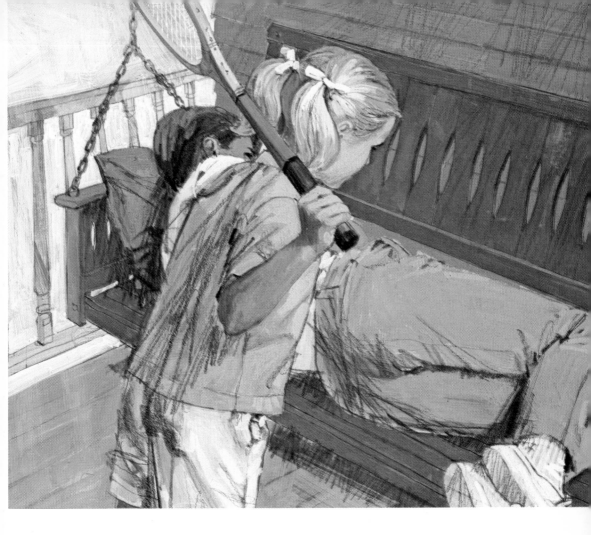

at thirteen, was small for her age, and her bobbing
twin ponytails made her look even younger. Where
all the force came from that she put into those
forehand drives, nobody could figure out.

Now, grumpily, Sally gave her brother up as a
lost cause and went out into the yard to practice
against the one opponent who was always ready to
take her on—the house. *Pow, pow, pow,* her ball
hit the smooth stretch of wall between the high-set

dining room window and the brick that stuck out just three feet above the ground.

Sally remembered the day, years ago, when she'd first discovered this exciting game. She'd found an old racket and a can of balls in the hall closet and immediately wanted to play with them.

"All right," her mother had said, "but let's learn to do it right."

So she had brought Sally out to this same spot and showed her the right way to hit a tennis ball —standing sideways to the house, holding the racket as though shaking hands with it, stroking with her full arm in a smooth half-circle that followed through after the ball left the racket. Sally was never bored another summer day. Nothing but a terrible thunderstorm could keep her from her favorite game.

Those first balls had been pretty dead. To get them to bounce at all, Sally had developed a mighty swing. Later, when her father brought home an occasional new ball for her—what a lovely, gleaming white, fuzzy treasure!—Sally was able to back up thirty feet and more from the house and still have the ball bounce back to her. Her right arm was almost as strong as Denny's.

Then, two years ago, Denny got a racket and began to learn the real game of tennis from the caretaker at the courts. Sally just had to learn, too. Endlessly she teased and begged her brother till at last he gave up and took her to the courts.

"Now, look," he explained patiently, "first point, you serve to my right-hand court; that's this square by the net. It's got to land inside these lines, see? Then, next point, you serve to this left-hand square. Hey, now, wait a minute! When you serve you toss the ball up in the air and hit it above your head."

"I like my way better," said Sally, dropping the ball behind the base line and swatting it over the net with a low drive. The ball landed in the right service court. Sally jumped up and down, her ponytails flopping. "My point! My point!"

"It is not your point because I didn't even try to hit it," Dennis said. "That isn't the right way to serve."

"Why isn't it? It worked, didn't it?"

In the end Dennis gave up trying to teach her to serve. He gave up teaching her a backhand, too; Sally, who had used only a forehand shot against the house, simply ran around the ball when it came to her left and returned it with that long, whistling drive that was so deadly. Sally's practice with the brick wall had paid off; by learning to place her balls between the window and the row of brick, she had developed a drive that just cleared the net and landed only inches within the base line.

"My point! My point!" she cried, driving the ball past Denny's reaching racket time and time again.

"Aw, nuts!" Dennis said at last. "You won't learn the rules, you won't learn any strokes you don't already know—all you want to do is win."

"Sure, why not?" Sally asked in surprise. "You're just mad because I beat you."

"You did not beat me! You can't beat a person when you don't play the game right. I'm through."

Dennis stalked off the court, leaving her angry and weeping. An amused and interested young man

who'd been watching the tennis lesson walked over to Sally and said, "Hit me a few."

It was Sally's first meeting with Mr. Cochran. And it was the beginning of the coaching that he had, with increasing interest, given both Barretts ever since.

His praise of them was rare. Mostly Sally and Dennis could judge their improving skill only by the fact that he continued to coach them. Under his stern gray eyes even Sally shut up and learned to toss a ball in the air and serve it overhand. It was a harder job to remember not to run around her backhand, but for Mr. Cochran she at least tried.

"You can't build a solid house on a weak base," he told her. "Every player has some strokes he's better at than others, but he won't be a champion till he's good at all of them."

Champion! Sally's eyes lighted at the word. "How soon am I a champion?"

The seriousness of Mr. Cochran's eyes gave way to a faint twinkle. "I'll let you know as soon as it happens," he promised.

Remembering that promise, Sally sighed a little. She'd been so sure that yesterday, when she won the Fairfield tournament, was the day. But when

Mr. Cochran had presented her with the cup, he'd said nothing but "Congratulations." He'd hardly even smiled. So Sally guessed she wasn't a champion YET. But maybe if she won the district tournament—

Splat, pow, the ball hit the bricks and rebounded clean and straight and hard. *Ping,* it sang as it connected with her racket strings.

To Sally there was music in the sound and the echo of a magic word.

Champion.

Several weeks later Sally and Dennis entered the district tournament in Maryville. Both won in their divisions, making them eligible to play in the state meet in Kirkland.

The following weeks were filled with projects for earning enough money for the tournament. Dennis said they'd need at least twenty dollars apiece to cover room, food, bus fare to and from Kirkland, and entry fees.

Things were going pretty well for Sally—money was coming in slowly, but it WAS coming in. Then one afternoon, in a fit of temper, she slammed a tennis ball against the house, splintering the dining room window and popping the two frayed strings in the center of her racket. Money for a new window and restringing her racket would eat up most of the precious tournament fund. And she couldn't ask Dad for the money, not the way things were at the shop.

Luckily the window was small. And luckier still, Dennis managed to tie the racket's broken strings. But the money spent to repair the window meant that she couldn't buy another tennis outfit. Her one-and-only would have to last all week—if she didn't get beaten in the early matches. If that happened, she wouldn't have to worry about clothes.

Sally got through three days of the tournament, and all the way to the semifinals when the strings in her racket popped and her money ran out. Tearfully she announced to Dennis that she was going back to Fairfield with him that night (Dennis had lost his match that afternoon).

"Champions don't cry," was his curt reply. He turned and walked away saying, "Go home, then —if you want to be a quitter."

Sally found her way back to the Y.W.C.A. and picked up her suitcase. She counted the change in her pocket—forty-five cents. That settled it; she couldn't stay another day even if she wanted to. And she didn't want to.

A hamburger and a glass of milk left her ten cents for fare to the bus station. She'd tucked six dollars for her ticket home in a corner of her suitcase.

Suddenly a bus turned the corner. "Oak and May" the sign read. That's the bus she and Dennis had taken to the club every day. Without really thinking about it, she climbed onto the bus and handed the driver her last dime.

It was getting dark when Sally reached the club. She slipped into a summer house and spent a damp, chilly, and spooky night in the swing.

The next morning she put on her tennis clothes, crunched down on the porch steps, hoping no one would notice her. Her clothes, dirty from three days of competition and one night of being wadded up in her suitcase, were a mess. And Sally Barrett was miserable.

People began to gather. The nets were up, and the courts quickly filled with players. The tournament manager arrived with the big draw sheets under his arm and tacked them up on the clubhouse porch. Referees climbed to their seats. The state tournament was beginning its fourth day.

It was late morning when Sally heard a girl's voice asking, "Where's Sally Barrett? Anybody here know Sally Barrett? I'm playing her in the semis."

Sally stood up slowly and went to meet Marjory Hicks. "I'm Sally Barrett," she said.

Marjory was tall and dark and slim; she looked sixteen. Her tennis outfit was beautiful and white, without a wrinkle in it. She looked at Sally in her crushed, none-too-clean clothes, and not the faintest sign of surprise disturbed her friendly smile.

"Hello," she said. "I believe we've got a match to play. How soon will you be ready?"

"I'm ready now," said Sally.

"Fine. We can get this first court here."

The tournament manager sent out a referee. He mounted the platform and announced loudly, "On the first court—a semifinal match in the Junior Girls' Division. Marjory Hicks, state junior girls' champion, Missouri Valley junior champion, playing Sally Barrett of Fairfield."

Sally felt as small as her name sounded. Quite a crowd collected to see Marjory play, and they clapped as the girls walked out on the court.

"Nobody even knows me," Sally thought sadly, "and they wouldn't clap if they did." She wondered what Denny had thought last night when he got on the home-bound bus and found she hadn't come.

"At least he knows I'm not a quitter, but—oh, dear, I wish he were here!"

Marjory served first. She had a powerful straight serve like a boy's. Sally blocked it, but its force nearly twisted her racket from her hand. Marjory had followed her service to the net. She followed with a neat volley. Sally ran for it. Her heart pounded and her knees shook, but she got the tip of her racket under the ball and pushed over a weak lob.

Marjory stepped back, figured its fall nicely, and smashed it for a placement.

Sally walked slowly back to the base line to wait for Marjory's next serve. That burst of speed had cost her her wind for a moment. She took deep breaths and tried to steady her knees. They felt like water.

"I'm hungry," she realized suddenly. "No wonder I can't run without falling to pieces."

Marjory's first service went out; her second serve was a much gentler shot that Sally returned with a cross-court drive. Sally had put all her strength into that drive, but it hardly went deeper than Marjory's service line.

"Grief!" Sally thought. "I can't be THAT hungry!"

She tried again a little later—and again. Hard as she strained, her drives kept coming down too soon. Instead of forcing Marjory back to the base line, they were allowing her to stand forward in the court within dangerously short distance of the net, where her volleys cost Sally point after point.

The points added up to three games lost, and Sally was just changing courts with Marjory when a blessedly familiar voice barked, "Here, you goop! Take this."

Sally grabbed for her brother instead of the racket he pushed toward her.

"Denny! You didn't go home!"

"Well, for Pete's sake, why would I? With you playing in the semis today."

"But you thought I was quitting—"

"Aw, I knew you'd be here," Denny said gruffly.

"Oh, Denny, I'm so GLAD to see you!"

Denny growled with embarrassment, "I'm sure not glad to see YOU—poppin' up those baby shots. Why didn't you tell me your racket broke again?"

Her racket! No wonder her shots had been falling short. Sally had forgotten the broken string. Overnight her strings had loosened; now her racket had no more bounce than a feather pillow.

Sally grabbed Denny's racket. "Thanks, Denny!"

Denny's racket was heavier than Sally's, and the handle was a half inch bigger around. Sally gripped it hard; it certainly didn't feel right. If she wasn't awfully careful to hang on to it, those balls

Marjory hit were going to twist it right out of her hand.

She served cautiously, and met Marjory's return with a blasting forehand. The ball went clear to the fence.

"Yipes!" Sally gasped. "This racket's a power-house!"

Denny had had his racket strung much tighter than anything Sally had played with before. Sally was accustomed to pouring all her strength into a shot, certain that it couldn't go beyond the base line. But, now, with Denny's racket, her lightest tap sent the ball boys backing way up against the fence to catch her balls.

"Steady, Sally," Dennis whispered when she changed courts again, five games down now. "Hold back on 'em, for Pete's sake!"

But Sally, fighting the racket and the heat, her light-headed tiredness and growing panic, was fast losing her small stock of patience. Steady, hah! That was easy enough for HIM to say!

Her anger grew as more points went against her. And then Marjory got over a whizzer, and Sally, blocking it too hastily, felt the racket turn in her hand. She dropped it like a red-hot potato.

"Ow! Ow!" she cried, shaking her blistered palm to cool it. The racket had twisted a bit of skin right off the ball of her thumb.

"Game and first set to Miss Marjory Hicks," the referee intoned. "She leads 6–0."

Marjory ran up to Sally. "May I get some tape? Would you like time out? I'll ask the referee."

"No, don't bother," Sally said crossly, but Marjory had already gone.

Sally slumped down on the side lines and rested her swimming head against her knees. She was licked. Her hand throbbed with pain; she was dizzy with hunger; the mounting heat of the sun closed in on her breathlessly.

Why had she stayed in Kirkland last night, when she could have gone home? Six–love. Why, she wasn't even giving Marjory a battle! She was just making a fool of herself—Sally Barrett, a little nobody from a country town upstate, trying to play a champion!

Champion. How Sally had dreamed of being a champion herself! But champions didn't get there by dreaming of it. They fought. They fought until there was no fight left in them—like Sally now. And then they fought all the harder.

Sally's head came up slowly. She looked at the racket that had brought her nothing but grief.

"It's a beautiful racket," she admitted. "If I'd only had time to get used to it—"

Time! Why, that was it! If she just had time.

"Here's the tape," Marjory said, hurrying back. "I'm sorry about your hand. What a nasty blister!"

"It doesn't matter," Sally said. Her voice came out different somehow, more grown-up sounding. "A little blister's nothing to cry about."

She taped the blister carefully. "Just one more minute, Marjory," she asked.

She walked over to Dennis. "My suitcase is on the porch, back of the swing," she told him. "There's six dollars in it. Will you take part of it and buy me some sandwiches? And a pint of milk. And a candy bar, or sugar cubes if you can get them."

Denny said uncomfortably, "That's bus fare, isn't it? How you figure to get home? I'm—I'm down to bus fare myself."

"I'll figure how to get home later," Sally said firmly. "Right now, I need that food."

Sally went straight to her base line. "Ready when you are," she called.

Marjory served. Sally hung on to her racket hard. It mustn't slip again. Under the tape she

could feel the steady throb of the blister. That was all right, though; it reminded her to hold that racket tight, tight, TIGHT.

She met Marjory's service with a defiant chop—a hard chop that spun like a bullet off Denny's racket. But its underspin made it a shorter shot than a drive. It stayed in court.

Marjory didn't seem to like chops a bit more than Sally; she had to loop her drive to get her return shot over the net. That made it a higher, softer ball. Sally cut it down with another chop.

Chop, return—chop, return. Sally tried a drive again. It went out. Chop, return—the points dragged endlessly to add up to a game. Marjory's game. But the winning of it had taken her almost as long as the whole first set.

The girls changed courts. Dennis was waiting at the net post. Sally took a big bite of the beef sandwich he held out to her, and a wonderfully refreshing swallow of milk. She tucked two sugar cubes into her cheek and felt them melt down her throat into energy. Some of the hollowness inside her disappeared. The ground was firm and hard again, no longer floating under her feet. Now she served with new zest.

Chop, return. Chop, return. The points accumulated. Sally's service gave her a slight advantage. She took the game—the first game she'd won.

The score remained tied. One–up. Two–up. Three–up, with each girl winning her own service game. Again Sally tried a top-spin drive, and again. They went out. Back she went to her steady, patient chop.

Four–up, and Marjory's service.

Marjory took the first point. And the second. Sally knew a brief moment of panic. "If she gets the games to five–four, she'll be just awfully close to winning." Only one service break away.

Sally tried another drive. The ball whistled low and hard across the net—and nipped chalk off the base line.

"Yahoooo!" Dennis yelled.

"Gleeps!" breathed Sally.

She had won more than a point. She had won the right to drive—and drive—and drive—straight through to victory. The racket was licked.

So was Marjory. Sally knew it that very moment. So did Dennis. And even Marjory must have known, though she fought for every point until Sally zoomed a final placement to her backhand corner and the referee shouted, "Third set and match to Miss Sally Barrett of Fairfield. She wins 0–6, 6–4, 7–5."

Marjory ran up to the net to take Sally's outstretched hand for the usual handshake. But Marjory reached across the net and gave Sally a friendly hug.

"Congratulations, Sally, you were great! I'm PROUD to lose to you. You've got all it takes to be a winner!"

"She has that," another voice said contentedly.

"Mr. Cochran!" Sally gasped. "How long have you been here?"

"Long enough to see some mighty pretty headwork—and heartwork, too. Yes, it was worth the drive down. I thought one of you kids must be putting on quite a show, or you'd have been home before this. So I decided to see what was going on."

Dennis said proudly, "She'll win tomorrow, Mr. Cochran. It'll be a breeze. I've seen her opponent play, and she isn't anywhere near so good as Marjory. Sally'll take her easy. Hey, whaddya know, Sally—tomorrow you'll be a champion!"

Mr. Cochran looked at Sally's blistered palm, patted it gently before he released it. His glance was amused and tender and something more as he glanced at her rumpled, dirty outfit and watched her wolf down the remaining sandwich.

"No, Dennis," he said, and to Sally his quiet voice rang out like a band on parade, "TODAY she is a champion!"

76

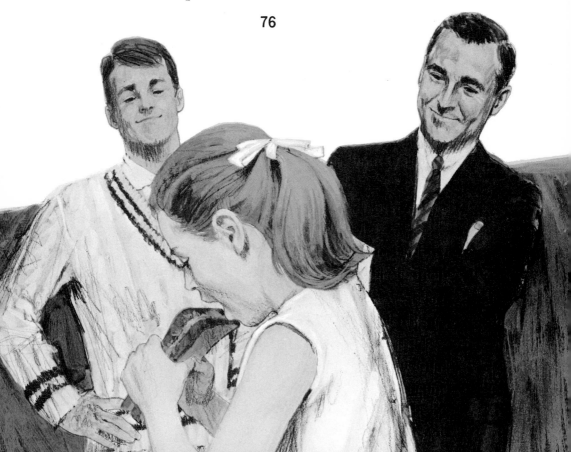

Unit Two   Men and Make-Believe

In Your Mind's Eye

Artists create pictures with paints, chalk, charcoal, and other media. Writers create pictures too, but with words. Their pictures can be seen only with the "mind's eye." These word pictures help create *sensory images* because they enable the reader to see, feel, taste, smell, and hear what the writer is describing.

The following paragraphs describe a ski run made by a boy named Ken. As you read, note the sensory images created by the author.

Ken dug his ski poles into the snow and thrust his weight forward. The sparkling snow, bathed in the late afternoon sun, slipped behind him as he glided into the ice-blue shadows of the West Wall. To Ken, his eyes unaccustomed to the sudden change in light, everything looked like a black-and-white photograph.

Gull-like he skimmed over the snow, barely touching it. Directly ahead lay a clump of yellow-green spruces. Scrawny and arthritic, they clung defiantly to the mountainside at timberline.

With a series of hop turns, Ken slalomed through the trees. Upon reaching open slope again, he crouched for the run to the North Glade. When he reached a level spot, he christied to a stop, sending a plume of snow arching through the air.

Far below, the lodge nestled in the mountain's lap. Surrounding the building was a multicolored disarray of skis and poles, like a fickle giant's unfinished game of pick-up sticks. A few yards to Ken's right, a snowshoe bunny popped out of the shadows. Suddenly something must have said "human," for he melted into the glade.

Ken looked over his shoulder, up the West Wall he had just skied. There were his tracks, a pair of silver ribbons, tying up the memory of a perfect day!

Is this a good description of skiing and the things Ken saw? Why or why not? How did you feel as you read it? Think about the following questions and discuss them.

1. What words does the writer use in the first paragraph to describe how things looked?
2. How does he describe the spruce trees? Can a tree be *arthritic*? Can it *cling* to the mountainside? How do these words help you form clear sensory images?
3. Is there such a thing as a *plume of snow*? Can a snowshoe bunny really *melt*?
4. What are some other examples of sensory imagery in this selection?

BOBBY BRONTOSAURUS

About 120 million years ago, the climate in many parts of our country was quite different from what it is today. Where now there are waving fields of wheat in the summer and howling blizzards in the winter, the land was covered with marshes and swamps and tropical rain forests.

Strange and fearsome-looking animals roamed the land, one of the largest of which was the brontosaurus. The brontosaurus is a member of the dinosaur family. Its name comes from two Greek words: *bronte* meaning *thunder* and *sauros* meaning *lizard.* This is a good name for this 40-ton monster, for when it walked its footsteps must have sounded like thunder.

But gradually the climate changed and the dinosaurs began to have some serious problems.

This is the fantastic story of Bobby Brontosaurus.

The first birds had just finished their studies at Song School. A flock of them circled their new home, earth, looking over the strange creatures with which they'd be living. The day was cool and the sun shone brightly. Suddenly a loud cry broke into the quiet afternoon.

"Mother! Mother! I can't move!"

The birds turned and flew toward the voice, landed in a nearby tree, and watched curiously.

"Mo-o-o-ther!" the voice cried painfully. "Mo-o-o-ther!"

Thump! Thump! Thump! The earth shook as a huge brontosaurus turned around and headed toward a smaller, screaming brontosaurus. The tree shook so much that two of the birds nearly fell out of it.

"Bobby, honestly!" Mrs. Brontosaurus sighed. "How many times do I have to tell you to watch where you're going!"

"I was just watching those little things up there." Bobby pointed his nose in the direction of the birds. "What do you think they are?"

"I haven't any idea," Mrs. Brontosaurus replied. "Things are changing so fast I can't begin to keep up with them any more. I have much too much on my mind to be bothered with little things."

Mrs. Brontosaurus pulled and tore at the tangled trees and vines that were caught on Bobby's tail.

As she tugged, she went on talking, partly to herself and partly to Bobby. "Yes, life isn't what it used to be. It's getting colder and drier. It gets harder and harder to find food. My stomach is growling half the time. I often wonder what's going to become of us." She stared thoughtfully into space.

"Is my tail free yet?" Bobby called back over his shoulder.

"Nearly," Mrs. Brontosaurus shouted back.

Bobby began lipping at a nearby fern.

"Stop that!" Mrs. Brontosaurus called sharply. "You know you shouldn't eat between meals!"

Bobby lowered his head.

"If you're not careful, you'll get as fat as your father," Mrs. Brontosaurus warned.

"I WANT to be big! I'm SUPPOSED to be big!" There were times when Bobby just couldn't understand his mother.

There was a loud crash, followed by Mrs. Brontosaurus' happy cry, "There! You're free, Bobby. Now watch where you're going."

Bobby lumbered along followed by his mother. He stopped before a delicate fern and started to take a bite.

"Bobby!" his mother roared.

"I forgot," Bobby replied.

"Your father ate and ate until he'd finished most of the food around here. Then he went off over the mountains in search of more. Nobody's seen or heard from him since. Nobody. I suppose he froze to death like all the others." A big tear glistened in the corner of Mrs. Brontosaurus' eye. "Promise you'll never wander away, Bobby. You must promise me. I get so lonely."

Bobby hated to see his mother looking so sad. "I promise," he said. "I'll stay with you, Mother, no matter what happens."

Bobby and his mother thundered along, leaving giant footprints and tail tracks as they went. As they climbed over a hill, Mrs. Brontosaurus stopped and looked into the valley below.

"You'll never believe this, Bobby," she said, "but when I was your age, this whole valley was filled with ponds and lakes, one right after the other. I could go for a swim any time I felt like it. And there were ferns—more ferns than you can believe. Now look around you. Hardly a pond in sight. And you know how hard it is to find enough to eat. All these changes are frightening. I keep wondering what the world's coming to."

Mrs. Brontosaurus thumped down the hill with Bobby close behind. "Mind you," she called back over her shoulder, "watch where you're going."

The curious birds circled above Bobby's head. Bobby stretched his neck to get a better look at one of them—it was so tiny—and the bird pecked Bobby's nose. Bobby pulled his head back in hurt surprise. He'd never seen anything like these small, feathered creatures before, and he wasn't at all sure he liked the newcomers.

"I wish I had someone to play with," Bobby said. "Cousin Jim, Uncle John, Aunt Mary—where have they gone? What's happened to everyone?"

"Bobby," Mrs. Brontosaurus began slowly, "I'd hoped you wouldn't ask about that until you were older. Everyone's disappeared. The truth is that we and all the other dinosaurs have been most un-wise. We've left our eggs lying around with nobody to watch them. Why, anyone could come along and eat them. And no one's ever cared enough to watch out for the newly hatched babies. Most of the youngsters just died off. Others have disappeared—

frozen or starved to death. I fear . . ." Mrs. Brontosaurus choked and sniffed loudly. "I fear . . . Why, it's terrible to think about.

"I'll never understand why we have such tiny brains. And the way we've been acting, we haven't even been using what we have! What a way for the rulers of the world to act!"

"Rulers? Are we really the rulers of the world?" Bobby cried.

"We're certainly the largest and strongest animals. Everyone fears us," Mrs. Brontosaurus said.

"Are we the wisest and bravest, too?" Bobby asked excitedly. "Rulers ought to be wiser and braver than anybody else in the whole world."

"We're brave, Bobby, there's no doubt about that. But wise? I've been trying to tell you how unwise we've been. It's all because of our tiny brains. Now, I want you to listen, Bobby. You must use your small brain carefully and keep your body healthy. Soon you will be the king. Soon you'll be the only brontosaurus left in the whole world."

"You'll be with me, Mother. You'll be the queen of the world, won't you?" Bobby's voice broke. "If you aren't, I'll be so lonely. It won't be any fun being king."

"Son, I'm getting old. Soon I'll have to leave you. When I'm gone, I hope you'll rule the world wisely and well." Mrs. Brontosaurus thundered along the valley toward a pond where it looked as though there might be enough ferns for dinner. Bobby dragged along behind his mother.

A big tear ran down the end of Bobby's nose and plopped to the ground. So much had happened. He'd learned so much about life and the world, he felt as if he'd grown up in one day.

When night came Bobby's heart was heavy. He kept looking at his mother as she slept. For the first time he realized how old and wrinkled she looked. He cried a little, but he knew that was no way for an almost-grown-up brontosaurus to act. Finally Bobby dropped off to sleep.

The songs of the birds awakened Bobby. He watched them dart happily back and forth overhead. Suddenly he noticed that his mother wasn't there. He began following her giant footprints from the clearing, hoping to find her nearby eating breakfast. But the tracks led far into the valley, across the plain, and disappeared into the mountains. She'd gone! She'd said she would, but Bobby never thought it would be so soon.

Loneliness covered Bobby like a huge black blanket. There was something terrible and frightening about being the last dinosaur. The very last dinosaur—the last king. The one and only king! Bobby's heart jumped. He was KING OF THE WORLD! Suddenly things weren't so bad.

"Listen, everybody," he shouted. "I'm your king. I'm your one and only ruler. Do you hear me? Are you listening?"

And that's the way the reign of King Bobby Brontosaurus began.

At first, things went very well in Bobby's kingdom. He was .well-loved by the birds and other animals and spent his days trying to make his kingdom a pleasant place to live.

But as time went on, Bobby spent more and more time thinking about how important he was. Being the very last dinosaur was, after all, quite an honor. It didn't happen every day.

King Bobby began to demand more and more from his subjects. He wanted to be waited on all the time. When he didn't get his way about something or when his subjects didn't move fast enough to suit him, he'd roar and stomp around. Bobby wouldn't listen to anyone and often pretended that he didn't even know his old friends any more. Being the last dinosaur, he kept thinking, was pretty important.

Bobby walked with his head so high that it often got caught in low-flying clouds. Once, because he had his nose so high in the air, he tripped over a tree and nearly broke a leg. Another time he narrowly missed stepping on two of his smaller animal subjects.

One day the animals called a secret meeting deep in the forest. After the meeting was called to order, one of the birds spoke. "King Bobby Brontosaurus was the first one I met when I came to earth. He was just a little fellow then—and a nice one, at that. But something has happened to the Bobby I knew. He's so selfish, power-hungry, so foolish. We must do something quickly, before we all die of unhappiness."

All the animals sat quietly and thought and thought. Then one of them suggested that they tie the trunk of a fallen tree to Bobby's tail. One of the birds said it wouldn't work. Hurting Bobby wouldn't necessarily make him a better ruler. It might even make things worse because he would just get angry.

All the animals were talking at once when the ground began to shake. There was a terrible crash as Bobby stomped into the meeting.

"I heard you! I heard every word you said! I'll punish you, every one of you!" Bobby was purple with rage.

"I'm king! I'll always be king! I'll live forever, and there'll never be anyone greater than I!" Bobby puffed his chest out and held his head higher than ever. "I am your king! Don't you forget it for one minute. I'm tired of hearing about my small head and my smaller brain. And I'm wiser than all of you put together! Why, even if I were small, I'd still be ruler because I'm so wise! Size has nothing to do with it!"

And with the last sentence, Bobby Brontosaurus began to shrink!

The animals stood in open-mouthed amazement.

"Size doesn't matter," Bobby cried as he shrank like a tired balloon. "It's how wise you are that counts." And he got smaller and smaller and smaller.

But no one paid any attention to Bobby's cries because he had shown that he was far from wise.

Bobby kept on shrinking. His tail and legs were almost the same shape, although they were much thinner. His body had shrunk more than his head and his neck had shrunk most of all.

Bobby scampered across the ground and ran under a flat rock. He peered up at the huge animals around him. One by one they turned and left the clearing. As they walked away, Bobby heard them discussing their new king. They didn't know who it would be, but they knew that they wanted someone who was wise. Maybe he'd be big, too. But most of all, he had to be wise.

A tiny tear ran down Bobby's cheek and dropped on the ground. Then another. And another. And another.

Bobby Brontosaurus' pride led to his downfall. Even today his great-great-great-great- (and so on) grandchildren, the lizards, crawl around with their heads very close to the ground.

Maybe they dream of being tall and poking their heads through the clouds and being king of the world. Maybe lizard mothers tell their lizard babies of their great-great-great-great- (and so on) grandfather, King Bobby Brontosaurus.

Who knows?

CARL AKELEY

THIS IS NOT A MUSEUM, BUT A WORKING
ESTABLISHMENT WHERE ALL ARE VERY BUSY!

So said the sign over the door of Ward's Natural
Science Establishment in Rochester, New York.
Inside the building young Carl Akeley and his
co-workers were indeed busy. They were preparing
the skins and skeletons of animals for display—an
art called taxidermy. Ward's was one of the few
establishments in 1885 where taxidermists could
practice their trade. Although Carl Akeley enjoyed his work, he was not happy.

"Hurry up with that zebra, Akeley," Professor
Ward shouted. "The museum wants it as soon as
possible."

"But, sir, I can't make it look lifelike in a short
time," Carl complained.

"We're running a business, not an art shop. Lifelike! Who cares?" Professor Ward exclaimed.

"Yes, sir," Carl sighed. "I'll do my best."

It seemed to Carl as if his dream of displaying
lifelike animals in a natural-looking setting would
never come true. *Maybe I should quit*, he thought
dejectedly.

Sadly his thoughts turned back to the zebra. He knew he could make a few careful cuts and remove the skin almost in one piece. That way, when he sewed the animal up for mounting, the stitches wouldn't show. But since the exactness of the work took time, he quickly made slits in the legs from hoofs to stomach. Just as he finished the cutting, the door of his workroom burst open. In rushed Bill Critchley, one of his co-workers.

"Say, Ake, have you heard the news?" the excited young man shouted.

"What news?" Carl looked up from his work.

"Jumbo, you know, Barnum and Bailey's famous circus elephant. He's been killed!"

"Oh? How did that happen?" asked Carl.

"The elephants were being unloaded from the railway cars that carry the show. It seems a small elephant crossed the tracks just as another train was coming. Jumbo managed to push his friend out of the way but was hit himself."

Carl shook his head. "That's a great loss to Barnum and to the children of America. Everyone loved to watch Jumbo lead the parade."

"That's just it," Bill went on. "Barnum doesn't want to lose him. Jumbo's body is still on the train tracks up in Canada. You and I are to go up there, bring him back, and mount him. That way Jumbo

can still travel with the circus. Old Ward will be in to tell you all about it in a minute."

On the train to Canada Carl and Bill thought about the huge task ahead of them. Neither had tried to mount such a large animal before. And by the time they got there, the elephant would have been lying in the sun for two days. The skin would be hard to work with and it certainly wouldn't smell very pleasant.

When Carl and Bill arrived at the railroad yards, they were met by P. T. Barnum. He spoke to the two young men. "Now, boys, you know Jumbo means a lot to the children. People expect to see him leading the parade, and I'm not going to disappoint them. I want him to be lightweight, yet sturdy enough to wheel through the rough streets on a platform in all kinds of weather. But this is the important part—he must look like he's alive! Can you do it?"

"Whew!" Bill whistled. "It will be hard enough just to put him together. Make him look alive? I don't see how it can be done. It's impossible."

It WAS a tall order. Nevertheless, Carl was jubilant. Here was the chance he'd been waiting for! *Impossible?* he thought. Then turning to Barnum he said, "In that case, sir, it may take us a while. Is five months too long?"

Barnum smiled at the confident young man. "It's September now. We're going into winter quarters. See that we have him by spring."

Even though the big elephant had started to decay, Carl took time to make careful measurements and sketches of the body. Then he and Bill hired six butchers from a local meat market to remove the skin. He boxed the bones and shipped them along with the skin to New York.

Back at Ward's a special building had to be constructed in order to have enough space for mounting the huge animal. Carl and Bill began to work even before the roof was on. They built a strong skeleton of oak beams following the measurements and sketches that had been made. Over this wooden skeleton they stretched the skin which had been specially prepared. They nailed it

to the wood so that the nails were hidden by lifelike wrinkles and folds.

By spring their masterpiece was ready, mounted on a huge wheeled platform. When it was rolled to the railroad station, people lined the streets and cheered. It looked just like the live Jumbo.

For many years Jumbo continued to lead the circus parade. Finally, he was retired. Today he can be seen in a museum in New England.

The people who looked at the mounted Jumbo were amazed at its lifelike appearance. Yet few thought about the work involved or the men responsible for it. But the work done on the elephant brought Carl Akeley to the attention of others interested in taxidermy. At the age of twenty-one, he had begun to make a reputation for himself, and soon he was given a chance to perfect his methods. Now taxidermy could become an art.

The realistic groupings of mounted animals in many museums today are largely due to the "impossible job" completed successfully by Akeley and his helpers on the beloved Jumbo.

1. Why was Carl Akeley unhappy with his work before his assignment on Jumbo?

2. Have you ever felt that you didn't have enough time to do a job well? When have you felt like this?

3. How would you describe P. T. Barnum? Do you think that you would have liked him? Why or why not?

The Hebrews blew a ram's horn to announce holidays, festivals, and the coming of the new moon. Our word **jubilant,** "rejoicing," comes from a Latin word, but is connected popularly with *yobel,* the Hebrew word for "ram's horn."

Pete At The Zoo

I wonder if the elephant
Is lonely in his stall
When all the boys and girls are gone
And there's no shout at all,
And there's no one to stamp before,
No one to note his might.
Does he hunch up, as I do,
Against the dark of night?

BARKHAM STREET

Edward

Edward Frost, who had his share of problems, didn't see how he'd ever solve the biggest one. This was Martin Hastings, the bully of Barkham Street. Martin was two years older than Edward, and there was no solution for this. Martin would continue to be two years older until he was a hundred and Edward was ninety-eight. Edward had a feeling that even then he might not be entirely safe.

The fact that he had only one enemy didn't help Edward much, because Martin lived next door to him. Edward lived at number 21 Barkham Street, and Martin lived at number 23. There was no solution for this, either. How could you avoid your enemy if every time you looked out a door he looked out a window and saw you?

"Why doesn't Dad get a job in Alaska, now that it's a state?" Edward asked his mother one day.

Mrs. Frost didn't look surprised at the question, but she said Edward's father couldn't very well change his job just like that. Mr. Frost was a teacher at a university in St. Louis.

"Alaska would be fun," Edward insisted, without much hope. "I'll bet there's a lot of room for teachers up there. I bet they need them badly. You'd think Dad'd want to go where he was needed."

Mrs. Frost sighed. "Is it Martin Hastings again?" she said.

Edward nodded.

"What did he do this time?"

This time Martin had chased him for blocks, and then, when Edward was absolutely exhausted and fell down, Martin sat on top of him and pulled his hair and said over and over, "Uncle, say UNCLE . . . ."

Martin was a big boy, and Edward not especially. It was an awful, grinding feeling to be sat on that way. And though Martin hadn't pulled hard it was terrible to have your hair pulled at all.

Edward had held out as long as he could, and then gasped, "Uncle," and was released. He got up shakily, dusted off his trousers, and walked away with Martin's voice loud in his ears.

"Don't forget, now," Martin yelled. "Whenever I look at you and wiggle my finger, you gotta say uncle. Understand, Weird One?"

Edward kept walking, not too fast, because that might start everything all over again, but without answering or looking back. He hated being called Weird One almost as much as he hated the pounding, but there was nothing he could do about that either.

There was no point in telling his mother all this, because it didn't so much matter what Martin did or said, it was just the fact that Martin was there, big and mean and living next door. It was the fact that Edward, looking ahead, could see no way in which any of this would be changed, unless Martin moved away or dropped dead. Neither seemed likely.

"I'm going to get a crew cut," he said now.

"That's fine," said his mother.

"I think I'll take a course in muscle-building, too. I'll write to one of those magazines about how you get your muscles like cannon balls, and then I'll poke him in the jaw and knock him out for a week and when he comes to I'll make him say uncle for a month without stopping."

"You can't do that. I mean, you can't take a strong-man course."

"Why not?"

"Because your muscles aren't developed yet."

"That's exactly what I'M saying," Edward pointed out. "I'm going to . . ."

"No," said his mother. "What I mean is, you aren't old enough for weight lifting and all that sort of thing. You have to be—oh, well into your teens before you can do such things."

"How well into them?"

"Fourteen, anyway, I should think."

"Oh, crums," said Edward in a gloomy voice.

Fourteen seemed practically as far away as ninety-eight. Maybe he should concentrate on learning to run fast. He supposed it was cowardly to run, but the sight of Martin looming around corners like a bear always got his legs into action before he had time to think. And if he HAD to run, the smart thing would be to run fast enough not to get caught.

"You know," his mother was saying, "even if we did move somewhere else, it wouldn't be much help, probably. I understand there's a bully on every block. I expect even Alaskan blocks. It's what the other mothers tell me at P T A meetings."

"What do the mothers of the bullies say?"

Mrs. Frost shook her head. "I guess maybe they often don't know. Martin Hastings' mother doesn't know. Or won't believe it. Nobody can tell her anything."

"I heard Ruth Ann's mother telling her one day. Ruth Ann's mother said Martin ought to be locked in an attic until he comes of age."

"Oh, but that's a dreadful thing to say."

"You know what he did? Ruth Ann and some girls were making a tea party for dolls in the back yard, and Martin went in and knocked everything over, except he drank the ginger ale—that was the tea."

Mrs. Frost looked unhappy. "Well, it was a bad thing to do."

"Ruth Ann's mother and Mrs. Hastings yelled at each other all over the place. Didn't you hear them?"

"I must have been away, thank heaven. Edward, I don't know what the answer is. But I'm just glad you aren't a bully."

Edward snorted. "Me? I'm the kind who runs."

"What else can you do? You needn't be ashamed of running if there's nothing else to do."

"Dad says I should stand up to him."

"How can you stand up to somebody twice your size?"

"Dunno," said Edward. But secretly, while liking his mother for understanding how hard it all was, he sort of agreed with his father. The trouble was that in order to stand up to somebody you had to remember to stand still, and he always forgot and ran. It was a problem, all right.

"I'm going to Rod's now," he told his mother. "We're going to finish our birdhouses today."

"Good. Are you taking your bike?"

"Yes."

"Well, watch out for cars. And be home by five o'clock."

"All right," said Edward, pulling on his jacket. He went out to the garage where he kept his bike. As he rode he looked around for Martin, and was relieved to see no sign of him.

Martin

As far back as he could remember, Martin had found Edward Frost a pain and a pest, about as pleasant to put up with as a nail in his shoe. A guy whose parents were forever fussing over him, taking him on picnics and to the zoo, turning up at school for assemblies and Parents' Nights. A guy whose mother ran the P T A and whose father had been seen pitching a ball to him night after night, week after week, until Birdbrain finally learned to get the bat on it. A guy who didn't have a brother, much less a sister, or any troubles at all, so far as Martin could see.

But there was one thing Edward didn't have that he wanted something awful. Something Martin had and Edward didn't. A dog. That was probably why he'd been even more of a nuisance than ever lately. Calling people names and then running home safe.

Martin had always been able to make Edward run, to make him say uncle, to make him cry, even. The times when he managed to make Edward or any other kid cry were in a way that Martin couldn't understand both the best and the most awful times for him. Somehow he would feel, watching the angry tears streak down a face in front of him, sort of relaxed and proud, sort of *that'll-show-them* (even if he didn't exactly know who *them* was). Then, when he'd hardly had time to feel that, he'd begin to get a little shaky, so he'd have to walk away very fast.

Today, hearing Edward call him *Fatso*, Martin forgot everything—the heat, his parents, his promises, even for one furious moment, his dog Rufus. He ceased to be Martin, desperately trying to turn over a new leaf, and became, in a wrathful upsurge, the bully of Barkham Street.

He took out after Edward, who could run fast but not faster than a wild person two years older and stronger, and in minutes he had Edward flat on the ground, pummeling him and pulling his hair.

"Uncle. Say UNCLE," Martin growled through his teeth.

Edward shook his head, as much as he could with his hair clutched in Martin's fist.

"You better, Weird One. I'm warning you," Martin told him.

"No," Edward gasped.

Martin tightened his grasp and shook Edward's head like a mop. "Say uncle!"

"Uncle," Edward choked out at last, and Martin let him go, watching while the smaller boy slapped the dust off his trousers and started away.

Feeling dissatisfied, not properly victorious at all, Martin shouted, "Don't you forget now! When I tell you to say uncle, you say uncle, PRONTO!"

"You fat dumbbell," Edward yelled, beginning
to run again now that he was close enough to make
it to his house in safety. "You could heat a building
with all that hot air!"

"Ah! The trouble with you is you're jealous,"
Martin shouted. "You can't have a dog because
you're such a slob your parents won't let you!"

Edward kept running, and Martin, breathing
hard and itching all over, slouched along in a state
of tumult.

"You young bully, why don't you pick on someone your own size?" said a quavery voice.

With a sense of being beset on all sides, Martin looked up and saw old Mr. Eckman standing on his porch, shaking a white fist. "Somebody ought to tell your parents on you," the old man yelled hoarsely.

"Mind your own business, Prune Face," Martin called up, and got a kick out of the look on old Eckman's countenance, which did, in fact, look sort of like a prune.

Except for his mother and father, there was no adult Martin wouldn't treat with reckless insolence. Even teachers, even the principal, even policemen. Grown-ups filled him with defiance. Always poking their noses into other people's business, thinking just because they were big they could push any kid around. And they always said that about picking on someone your own size, which was pretty dumb of them. The whole point was WINNING, getting somebody angry or scared. How could you do that with a guy your own size? If he pulled off Otto's cap, for instance, and threw it up in a tree, something he often did to Edward's, would Otto run yelling home? He would not. He'd take a poke at Martin, that's what he'd do. And Martin wasn't sure—not exactly sure—just what he, himself, would do then. Maybe poke back. Maybe run? He just wasn't about to find out.

Leaving Mr. Eckman furious, Martin walked along home faster, hoping that his mother hadn't by any chance stopped work early.

He passed Edward Frost's house, next door to his own, looking to see if Edward was hanging around the safety of his yard, ready to yell *Fatso*, or *Plump Pudding*, before diving through the door. There was no sign of him. Probably inside, complaining to his mother, Martin thought scornfully. Edward's mother, of course, would be there. She always was, afternoons, with cookies and stuff for Edward and his friends.

At his house he was relieved to see the garage doors open, the garage itself empty. His father used their old car to drive to the office, and his mother had the newer one out on her job. She sold cosmetics in people's houses, and it kept her pretty busy afternoons. Martin had never minded, or anyway not very much, and it wouldn't have mattered if he had minded, because the Hastings family needed the extra money she made. He hoped that his dopey sister, Marietta, was out, too, visiting some of her dopey friends.

In the old days, before Rufus, it hadn't bothered him much, coming home to an empty house.

Sometimes he played the radio so loud it practically made the walls shiver. Sometimes he poked around in his father's file box, which was forbidden and pretty dull when you got in it. Sometimes he just stamped around from room to room, blowing his bugle and planning how when he grew up he would always have a house to himself. He was never going to get married or have a family, that was for sure. The second he got old enough, he was going to go somewhere far away and have lots of friends and a dog, but no relatives.

The word **magazine** comes by way of the French language from the Arabic word *makhazin*, "a storehouse for supplies." Books were so-called because they too were "storehouses of knowledge."

The Tale of Custard the Dragon

Belinda lived in a little white house,
With a little black kitten and a little gray mouse,
And a little yellow dog and a little red wagon,
And a realio, trulio, little pet dragon.

Now the name of the little black kitten was Ink,
And the little gray mouse, she called her Blink,
And the little yellow dog was sharp as Mustard,
But the dragon was a coward, and she called him
    Custard.

Custard the dragon had big sharp teeth,
And spikes on top of him and scales underneath,
Mouth like a fireplace, chimney for a nose,
And realio, trulio daggers on his toes.

Belinda was as brave as a barrel full of bears,
And Ink and Blink chased lions down the stairs,
Mustard was as brave as a tiger in a rage,
But Custard cried for a nice safe cage.

Belinda tickled him, she tickled him unmerciful,
Ink, Blink, and Mustard, they rudely called him
    Percival,
They all sat laughing in the little red wagon
At the realio, trulio, cowardly dragon.

Belinda giggled till she shook the house,
And Blink said Weeck! which is giggling for
   a mouse,
Ink and Mustard rudely asked his age,
When Custard cried for a nice safe cage.

Suddenly, suddenly they heard a nasty sound,
And Mustard growled, and they all looked around.
Meowch! cried Ink, and Ooh! cried Belinda,
For there was a pirate, climbing in the winda.

Pistol in his left hand, pistol in his right,
And he held in his teeth a cutlass bright,
His beard was black, one leg was wood;
It was clear that the pirate meant no good.

Belinda paled, and she cried Help! Help!
But Mustard fled with a terrified yelp,
Ink trickled down to the bottom of the household,
And little mouse Blink strategically mouseholed.

But up jumped Custard, snorting like an engine,
Clashed his tail like irons in a dungeon,
With a clatter and a clank and a jangling squirm
He went at the pirate like a robin at a worm.

The pirate gaped at Belinda's dragon,
And gulped some grog from his pocket flagon,
He fired two bullets, but they didn't hit,
And Custard gobbled him, every bit.

Belinda embraced him, Mustard licked him,
No one mourned for his pirate victim.
Ink and Blink in glee did gyrate
Around the dragon that ate the pyrate.

Belinda still lives in her little white house,
With her little black kitten and her little
　　gray mouse,
And her little yellow dog and her little red wagon,
And her realio, trulio, little pet dragon.

Belinda is as brave as a barrel full of bears,
And Ink and Blink chase lions down the stairs,
Mustard is as brave as a tiger in a rage,
But Custard keeps crying for a nice safe cage.

Implied Information

In the following paragraphs, certain things are *implied*. That is, even though you will not find direct answers to the questions which follow, you will find *clues* to the answers.

Read the paragraphs, then answer the questions. Discuss the clues which helped you arrive at your answers.

The clock in the town hall struck three. A cloud darkened the sun, and a gust of wind blew smoke from the smouldering leaves into Jody's face. "Ow!" he cried as he dropped the rake and covered his eyes with his hands.

Just then the kitchen door opened. "Jody," Mrs. Davis called, "please come in and watch Mary Lee while I take some things to the attic. Don't forget to put your bike in the garage. It's supposed to snow tonight."

1. Is it 3 a.m. or 3 p.m.?
2. What is Jody's last name?
3. Is Jody a boy or a girl?
4. What time of year is it?
5. Why did Jody drop the rake?
6. In what part of the country might Jody live?
7. Where could Jody not possibly live?
8. Is Mary Lee older or younger than Jody?
9. Does Jody live in town or on a farm?

THE HARE AND THE WIDOW

Southeast of the great city of Nairobi, past the National Park to the Athí Plain, there is a roadway that touches Kitui. On the north side of this road lives one group of the Wakamba people, and on the south live the Masai. Distinctive, interesting folk they all are, but this story takes place in the land of the Wakamba, where people delicate of feature, skilled in the artistic carving of wood, noted for spectacular dancing that includes fantastic leaps in the air and double somersaults, live peacefully on their grassy pastures, tending their herds, sowing their fields, and sometimes serving with distinction in the Kenya army.

Any sunny day you can see, as you drive along the road, hundreds of curious objects hanging in the trees. They look like short logs, suspended from the branches, and that is what they are, except that they are hollowed out of gum-tree branches or sisal stems and lidded at both ends with a circular piece in which holes are bored. These structures are then tied with string in the middle and in that string is inserted a branch of wood crooked at the top so that it will fit over a tree limb and turn gently in the wind.

These are beehives.

For, you see, the Wakamba people of today love honey just as much as did the people of long ago, and they tell many stories about this sweet and the animals, as well as humans, who had a passion for it.

Hare had an inordinate love of honey, and since he could not climb the hollow trees to get it, he always had to resort to other means.

In those long-ago days human beings and animals had one common language; they lived together and worked together and shared many of life's experiences.

Hare, who had noticed that the lands of a certain rich old widow were abundant with bees and honey, went to her and asked for work.

"Well and good," answered the rich old widow. "I have a piece of work that needs doing, and I will be more than glad of your help."

"Show me what is to be done," said Hare.

So the rich old widow hobbled out a way with him and pointed out, in the distance, certain lands that she wished him to clear, dig and plant with various crops.

"As you see," she told Hare, "I am lame and old, and my eyesight is poor, so I will not visit the fields very often. You may come to me each evening for your pay."

"Dear lady," said Hare, "I shall not ask much, for I take pity on your afflictions. If you can only spare me a pot of honey each day, I shall be happy, for that is my favorite food."

To this the widow happily agreed, and so the bargain was made.

Every morning thereafter, bright and early, Hare passed the widow's house, giving her a hearty hello on his way to the fields, and every evening he stopped on his way back to collect his pot of honey.

As you may know, none of the hare family is particularly fond of work. They prefer lazing in the woods, sleeping, or having a good gossip with friends to soiling their handsome coats with honest toil, and this hare was no exception. He pleased himself all day long, day after day, frolicking and gamboling, never once clearing or hoeing the earth.

One day the rich old widow said to him, "Are you about finished with the clearing and cultivating?"

"Not yet," answered Hare. "The fields are very large."

"Tomorrow I shall go with you to the fields to see how you are getting on," said the widow, and nothing he could say would dissuade her.

Hare was in a panic, for he had let the days go by without touching the fields, but he put his clever, tricky mind to work on a solution to his problem.

Next morning, instead of leading the widow to her own fields, he took her to a well-tilled shamba close by, owned and worked by an industrious neighbor. This field had been beautifully cleared, cultivated, and prepared for seeding. It was a work of art, and Hare showed her about with pride.

You may imagine the widow's pleasure. She was so proud of her efficient, hard-working employee that she gave him an extra pot of honey that evening.

Matters continued in this way for a long time. Whenever the widow wished to visit her fields, Hare simply took her to other people's shambas, and the nearsighted old lady continued to be pleased with his work and to reward him well.

At last, however, the planting season arrived, and the widow gave Hare the seed to be sown on her land. He took it away, and every day busied himself as before, skylarking, except that now he had much grain to eat, and daily he grew fatter.

Of course, harvest time was fast approaching, but Hare, who by this time had had plenty of practice in lying and evasion, was not worried; he merely continued to enjoy himself.

Finally, though, the time came when he had to show her the ripened grain, for she was determined to harvest it herself. So on the appointed day he simply led the widow into her industrious neighbor's field and told her to harvest.

Happily she began to gather the maize. She sang as she severed the ears, took off the shucks, and piled the fat cobs in the field. How rich was the harvest, she thought, and how kind and faithful her employee, who was responsible. Not even a half-blind, crippled old widow could be unfortunate as long as she had such a friend.

Suddenly there came to her ears the sound of angry shouts and running feet. The real owner of the field appeared with his sons, full of indignation. They beat the widow with sticks and drove her away, refusing to listen to her protests. Bruised, weeping, and sore, she crept home and told her neighbors, and they set out to look for Hare, promising to find him and bring him to justice.

Naturally he was not to be seen anywhere, for he had taken the precaution of leaving the area, and was now safely hidden in the bush, miles away.

Unfortunately they had to return without him, but they never forgot what he had done. They pursued every hare they could find and dealt with all of them mercilessly, and even today you will notice that people hunt Hare's descendants with sticks, stones and snares. Whenever they catch one they generally put him in a pot. His flesh is remarkably sweet and good to eat, they say; perhaps that is because he has always been fond of honey.

In the Middle Ages, the **toil** of knights in armor was usually a battle. The Middle English word *toilen* meant "to stir up or struggle." You may toil and struggle over a particular task, but you are just working long and hard at it.

MONSTERS OF MYTH AND LEGEND

Do you ever look closely at clouds floating by and imagine that they are strange animals? Or do you like to write stories about beasts?

Inventing beasts is an age-old pastime. While we know that creatures like the dragon are only imaginary, for thousands of years people accepted them as real.

In general, the fantastic monsters that appear in myth and legend are of three types.

I. Composite animal beasts, which are a combination of several known animals.

II. Composite human-animal beasts, which are a combination of both human and animal forms.

III. Single beasts, which are unlike any living thing, past or present.

I

Cockatrice. The cockatrice is a deadly monster which hatches from a yolkless egg laid by a cock. Part cock and part snake, the cockatrice has the head of a cock, toadlike eyes, large pointed wings, and a yellow snakelike tail which curls over his yellow body.

Although he is only two feet long, the cockatrice is dangerous because his breath, or even sight of a cockatrice, is fatal to a man. Because of his small size, this beast can hide quite easily, then attack without warning.

About five hundred years ago an old cock was actually put on trial in Europe on the charge of

having laid an egg. It was not unusual that a trial was held because animals, like humans, had to account for their actions. No one doubted that a cock could lay an egg, but such a thing was rare. The egg was supposed to contain a cockatrice. No wonder that the old cock was sentenced to death. He was responsible for bringing a terrible creature into the world!

There is only one sure way to kill a cockatrice. Since the sight of the beast can kill not only a man, but also the monster himself, cockatrice hunters used to cover themselves with mirrors.

Belief in cockatrices began to die out in the seventeenth century, but even then "Cockatrice Killed" appeared along with "Corns Controlled" and "Coughs Cured" in the indexes of some medical books.

Griffin. The griffin is a monster whose head, neck, wings, and forelegs are those of an eagle and whose body, tail, and hind legs are those of a lion. Half eagle, half lion, it is so large that you can easily make drinking vessels from its claws. Since the griffin represents the sun's golden wealth, he is the guardian of gold mines and hidden treasures of the fabled lands near India.

According to a legend of the Middle Ages, two huge griffins spread their wings to catch the rays of the rising sun and then fly across the heavens until sundown.

These beasts line their nests with gold. It is said that if a man could collect the gold from just one nest, he would be rich for life. However, griffins are very fierce. Anyone who tries to take a griffin's treasure can expect to be torn to pieces by the beast's sharp claws.

In Europe people long believed that the tusks of an extinct rhinoceros found in northern Asia were actually the claws of the griffin.

II

Sphinx. One of the most famous monuments in the world is the Great Sphinx of Egypt. The 240-foot-long body of this huge stone monster resembles that of a lion. The head, which rises 66 feet above the desert, has the form of a man's head. For over 5,000 years the Great Sphinx has rested on the sand at the entrance of the Valley of the Nile.

In ancient times many smaller statues of sphinxes were constructed as guards for Egyptian tombs. Because of this, and for other reasons, the sphinx appears to have been a symbol of death. But why men gave it the form of a man-lion is uncertain.

The Greeks probably borrowed the sphinx from the Egyptians, but they changed the monster's appearance. The Greek sphinx has the head of a woman, the body of a lion, and the wings of a great bird. To the Greeks, the sphinx symbolized the mysterious—the meaning most frequently given the sphinx today.

According to a Greek legend, the sphinx sat on a cliff outside the city of Thebes. No person was allowed to pass without answering this riddle: "What animal walks on four legs in the morning, two legs at noon, and three legs at night?"

When a traveler gave the wrong answer—and that always happened—she threw him from the high cliff to the rocks below. Naturally, few people wished to visit Thebes.

One day a young man named Oedipus, unaware that he was really the son of the king of Thebes, approached the city. To the Sphinx's riddle the young man replied, "A man—for he walks on four limbs as a child, two as an adult, and as an old man he uses a cane."

The Sphinx, on hearing the correct answer, was so upset that she threw herself over the cliff. Oedipus was proclaimed king for freeing Thebes from the curse of the Sphinx, and the city became a safe place to visit.

Centaur. Many centuries ago the Greeks believed in a man-horse beast they called a centaur. There were supposed to be two kinds of centaurs—those who were wild and terrorized the land, and those who were wise and friendly.

One of the wisest centaurs was skilled in hunting, music, and medicine. According to a Greek myth, he was the teacher of many of the gods. One of his pupils became such an excellent doctor that it was said that he could bring the dead back to life.

When the wise old centaur died, he appeared in the heavens as a star in the constellation Sagittarius.

Scorpio

Capricornus

Sagittarius

Constellation

Astrological Symbol

III

Dragon. Stories of dragons can be found in nearly every part of the world, but their appearance and temperament differ greatly. We read of two main types of dragons.

The dragon described in European literature was usually evil. He looked somewhat like a huge scaly lizard. Although he had wings, he seldom flew; he preferred to haunt forests, wells, fountains, and all out-of-the-way places. He could destroy whole cities with his fiery breath. All dragons were supposed to possess great treasures which they jealously guarded. Ancient heroes were said to have fought with dragons to obtain their wealth. A creature of the night, the European dragon was the symbol of terror.

The Oriental dragon was very different. His body was longer, his head horselike and whiskered, and his ears two horns. He could change his size at will.

The Oriental dragon was a symbol for water. According to the stories, his breath formed clouds instead of fire, and when the monster climbed heavenward in spring, the weight of his feet on the clouds caused rain. Lightning flashed from the dragon's eyes, and wind resulted from his swift passing. Dragons fighting in water and air caused

floods or storms. Belief in these stories delayed the scientific study of weather for many centuries.

The Oriental dragons were not as fearsome as the European ones; they were friends and teachers of wise men and kings. Although these beasts possessed great treasures, they were generous with them. People who visited dragon kings often came away rich. As a rule, these monsters were kindly but unreliable.

As late as 1884 a Chinese newspaper printed a story about a dragon which was said to be living in a well, high up on a mountain. Belief in dragons has not died completely. Even today in some areas of China an eclipse is believed to be caused by a dragon hiding the sun.

Phoenix. One of the most colorful of the legendary monsters is the phoenix. Usually this bird is described as resembling an eagle whose body is covered with deep purple, blue, and rose feathers, with a ring of gold feathers around his neck. On his head is a bright tuft like that of a peacock.

According to one tale, there is a land far beyond India where death is unknown. It is a place of eternal spring where there is no sorrow, no hunger, no darkness. The fountain of youth is believed to be there. This wonderland is the home of the phoenix.

For one thousand years, only one such bird lives in this paradise, feeding only on pure air. Then at the end of a thousand years the phoenix leaves its paradise where death is unknown and flies across India to Arabia. There it gathers wood and spices. The bird continues its flight until it reaches the country of Phoenicia where it builds a nest of the wood and spices in the tallest palm tree. At dawn the phoenix turns toward the east as sparks from the rising sun set fire to the nest, and the bird dies in the flames. From the ashes rises a new phoenix.

As soon as the new bird is strong enough, it takes the nest with the ashes of its parent and flies to the City of the Sun. There it leaves the ashes as an offering, then continues on its way to the far-off paradise which will now be its home for a thousand years.

The legends of many countries contain a phoenix-like bird, although the details of the stories differ. For example, the life span varies. Some of the figures given are 350—500—540—1,000—1,460—and 7,006 years. The place and manner of life and death also vary, as do the names by which the bird is known. But in most legends, the phoenix represents the idea of life after death. It also is a symbol of the sun which—like the bird—dies in its own flames each evening and is born anew each morning.

The monsters of myth and legend hold an important place in the literature of the world. There you will be encountering the beasts you have just read about and many others.

Genius

Unicorn

Hydra

Mermaid

1. Why do you suppose that after awhile people began to believe these stories as truths?

2. What explanation do you suppose people gave for the existence of Genius, the monster illustrated at the top of this page?

3. Why have men always tried to explain things that are mysterious? Do all men do this, or only some?

4. In what ways are an Egyptian sphinx and a centaur similar? In what ways are these two creatures different?

A Lucky Thing

A Snap-Dragon will never snap
He's only wild in name.
Standing in a garden bed
The poor thing's very tame.

Nor does a Dande-Lion roar
Which is a lucky thing:
With all the millions that there are
That would be frightening.

DAVID AND THE PHOENIX

David knew that one should be prepared for anything when one climbs a mountain, but he never dreamed what he would find that June morning on the mountain ledge. He heard someone talking behind the bushes, and when he crawled through to investigate, he thought his heart would stop.

1: In Which David
   Meets the Phoenix,
   and There Is a
   Change in Plans

There stood a huge bird. David had been to the zoo, and at home he had a book of birds with colored pictures. He knew the more common large birds of the world: eagles, cranes, storks. But THIS bird—! Its shape was like that of an eagle, but stouter. Its neck had the length and curve of a swan's neck. Its head was again like an eagle's, with a hooked bird-of-prey beak, but the expression in its brown eyes was mild. The long wings were blunt at the tips, the tail was short and broad. The legs, feathered halfway down, ended in clawed feet. Its feathers sparkled, reflecting sunlight from the scarlet crest, the golden neck and back, the breast of silver, the bright blue wings and tail. Its size alone would have been enough to take David's breath away. He could have stood beneath the curve of that neck with room to spare.

But the most astonishing thing was that the bird had an open book on the ground and was apparently trying to learn part of it by heart.

"*Vivo, vives, vive,*" the bird read, very slowly and distinctly, staring hard at the book.

"*Vivimos, vivís, viven.* THAT is simple enough, you blockhead! Now, then, without looking." It cleared its throat, looked away from the book, and repeated in a rapid mutter: "*Vivo vives vive vi*—ah—*vivi*—oh, dear, what IS the matter with me?" Here the temptation to peek overcame it for an instant, and its head wavered. But it said, "No, no!" in a firm tone, looked carefully the other way, and began once more.

"*Vivo, vives, vive*—quite correct so far. Ah—*vi*—ah—oh, dear, these verbs! Where was I? Oh, yes, *vivo*—"

David's head reeled as he watched this amazing performance. There was no need to pinch himself to see if he were dreaming: he was perfectly wide awake. Everything else around him was acting in a normal way. The mountain was solid beneath him, the sunlight streamed down as before. Yet there was the bird, unmistakably before him, studying its book and speaking to itself. David's mind repeated over and over again: "What on EARTH? What on EARTH?" But of course there was no answer to that question. And he might have stayed hidden there all day, staring out at the bird and marveling, had it not been for a bee which came droning into the thicket straight for him.

He had a horror of bees, ever since he had once bumped into a hive by mistake. When he heard that dread sound approaching, his whole body broke into a sweat. All thought of the bird was immediately driven from his head. He could tell from the noise that it was one of those big black-and-yellow fuzzy bees, the ones with the nasty tempers. On it came, buzzing and blundering through the leaves. Suddenly it was upon him, so close that he could feel the tiny breeze stirred up by its wings. All self-control vanished. He beat at it wildly with his hands, burst out of the thicket and smashed into the bird before he could stop himself.

With a piercing squawk the bird shot into the air, flipped over, and came fluttering down facing

him—claws outstretched, hooked beak open, eyes a-glare. Completely terrified, David turned and bolted for the thicket. He managed to thrash halfway through when a vine trapped his feet. He pitched forward, protecting his face with his arms, and was caught up short by a dead branch snagging his shirt.

He was stuck. This was the end. He closed his eyes and waited, too numb with fear to cry out.

Nothing happened. Slowly he turned his head around. The bird seemed undecided whether to attack or flee.

"What, may I ask, are you doing here?" it said at last, in a severe voice.

"I—I—I was taking a walk," David said faintly. "I'm awfully sorry if I bothered you."

"You should not have come up here at ALL," the bird snapped.

"Well, I'm really sorry. But there was a bee in the bush here. I—I didn't mean to . . ." The fright had been too much. Tears started in David's eyes, and his lip began to tremble.

The bird seemed reassured, for its manner softened. It lowered and folded its wings, and the glare faded from its eyes.

"I'd go away," David mumbled, "only I'm stuck."

The bird looked at his dismal face and began to fidget awkwardly. "There, there," it said, "I had no intention of—I am afraid that I—stuck, did you say? Very easily mended, my dear fellow! It's just a question of—here, let me look." It crashed through the thicket to where David was caught and thrust its head down through the branches. Its muffled voice came floating up. "Take heart! There seems to be—aha! just so—One moment, please—bit of vine—THERE we are!" There was a snapping sound from below, and David's foot was released. He unstuck the snag from his shirt, pushed his way out of the thicket, and sat down weakly on the grass. Whew! At least the bird was not going to harm him. It seemed to be quite a kindly creature, really. He had just frightened it and made it angry by bursting out of the bushes so suddenly.

He heard a thrashing in the thicket, followed by the bird's anxious voice: "Hello! Are you still there?"

"Yes. What—?"

There were more sounds of struggle. "This is rather awkward. I—the fact is, I am afraid, that I am stuck myself. Could you—"

"Yes, of course," said David. He smiled to himself, a little shakily, and re-entered the thicket. When he had disentangled the bird, the two of them sat down on the grass and looked at each other. They hesitated, not quite sure how to begin.

"I trust," said the bird at last, "that you are not of a scientific turn of mind?"

"I don't know," said David. "I'm interested in things, if that's what you mean."

"No, it is not. There is a great deal of difference between the interest shown by normal people and the uncontrollable interest of scientists. You are not, I hope, acquainted with any scientists?"

"No."

"Ah," said the bird, with a relieved sigh. "Everything is quite all right, then. I do hope that you will forgive me. I am not usually so rude. The fact is that you gave me quite a horrible start."

"Oh, I'm sorry I frightened you."

"Frightened, my dear fellow?" said the bird testily. "I am never frightened. I do not know the meaning of the word."

"What I mean is," David said quickly, "that you frightened ME." This seemed to satisfy the bird; and David, to heighten the good impression, added: "Golly, you looked fierce."

The bird smiled. "I CAN rise to a terrifying ferocity when angered. A noble strain of fighting blood courses through my veins. Not that I go out of my way to seek trouble, you understand. Quite the other way around. 'Peaceful' could well describe my general bearing. Meditative. I am usually to be found Thinking. I have a powerful intellect. No doubt you have noticed the stamp of genius on my brow."

David supposed that the bird meant its scarlet crest, and he nodded. "That's one of the first things I noticed about you."

"Indeed?" cried the bird delightedly. "You are certainly more alert than most! But, as I was saying, I am usually to be found Thinking. The first condition of Thinking is solitude. And that, I fear, is a desire most difficult of realization."

"I beg your pardon."

"People," explained the bird, "do not leave you alone."

"Oh," said David. He blushed, thinking that the words had been aimed at him, and began to get up. But the bird signaled him to remain where he was.

"I do not mean YOU, my dear fellow. I assure you that I am delighted to make your acquaintance. It is all the others. Do you know that I have spent the greater part of my life being chased? I was driven out of Egypt like a common game bird. Out of the mountains of Greece, too. The desert of Africa, the Arabian wilds—no matter where I fled, people would come prying and peering and sneaking after me. I have tried Tibet and China—with the same result. At last I heard of a region where there was peace, where everyone lets everyone else alone. Here, I thought, I should—"

"Pardon me for interrupting. Where?"

"Why, here, to be brief," said the bird, waving its wing toward the valley. "Here, I thought, I

should be able to breathe. At MY age one likes a little quiet. Would you believe that I am close to five hundred years old?"

"Golly!" said David. "You don't look it."

The bird gave a pleased laugh. "My splendid condition DOES hide my years. At any rate, I settled here in the hope of being left alone. But do you think I was safe?"

David, seeing that he was supposed to answer no, shook his head.

"Quite right," sighed the bird. "I was not. I had been here no more than three months when a Scientist was hot on my trail. A most disagreeable fellow, always sneaking about with field glasses, a camera, and, I fear, a gun. That is why you startled me for a moment. I thought you were he."

"Oh," David cried, "I'm awfully sorry. I didn't bother you on purpose. It's just that I never saw a mountain before, so I climbed up here to see what one looked like."

"You climbed up here."

"Yes."

"Climbed," said the bird, looking very thoughtful. "Climbed... I might have known... It proves, you see, that the same thing could be done again by someone older and stronger. A very grave point."

"Oh, I see," said David. "You mean the—"

"Exactly! The Scientist. He is, I fear, very persistent. I first noticed him over there"—the bird waved its wing toward the opposite side of the valley—"so I removed to this spot. But he will undoubtedly continue his search. The bad penny always turns up."

"Oh, dear, that's terrible!"

"Your understanding touches me," said the bird huskily. "It is most unusual to find someone who cares. But have no fear for me. I am taking steps. I am preparing. Imagine his disappointment when he arrives here and finds me flown from the nest. I am, to be brief, leaving. Do you see this book?"

"Yes," said David. "I heard you reading it, but I couldn't understand it. Is it magic?"

"No, my boy, it is Spanish. I have chosen a little spot in the Andes Mountains. South America, you know. And of course one must be prepared. I am learning Spanish so that I shall be able to make my way about in South America. I must admit that I hate to leave. I have become very fond of this ledge. It is exactly suited to my needs—perfect climate, magnificent view..."

They fell into a lengthy silence. The bird gazed sadly out over the valley, and David rested his chin in his hands and thought. The mystery was clearing up. The bird's presence on the mountain and the fact that it had been reading a book were explained. And so natural was its speech that David found himself accepting it as nothing unusual. The thing that worried him now was that the bird would soon leave. Here they had only just met, and already the promise of a most interesting friendship was melting. The bird had taken time to talk to him and explain things to him as though he were an equal. And although he did not understand many of the long words it used, he felt pleased at being spoken to as though he did understand. And the bird knew all about faraway countries—had visited them and lived in them and had adventures in them for almost five hundred years. Oh, there were so many things David wanted to know and ask about! But the bird was leaving. If only he could talk it into staying, even for a short while! He could try, anyhow—after all, the bird had said itself that it did not want to go.

"Bird—" He stopped, and blushed. It was hard to put into words.

"Yes, my boy."

"Well—I—I don't believe I know your name," David stammered, unable to get the real question out.

"Ah, forgive me!" cried the bird, jumping up. "Permit me the honor of presenting myself. I daresay my name is familiar to you, celebrated as

it is in song and story. I am the one and only,
the Unique, Phoenix." And the Phoenix bowed
deeply.

"Very glad to meet you," said David. "I'm
David."

"Delighted, my dear fellow! An honor and a
pleasure." They shook hand and wing solemnly.
"Now as you were saying—?"

"Well, Phoenix, I was just thinking," David
stammered. "It's too bad—I mean, couldn't you—
it would be nice if we—Well, do you really HAVE
to go to South America? It would be nice if you'd
stay a while, until the Scientist shows up anyway
—and I like talking with you . . . " His face burned.
It seemed like a lot to ask.

The Phoenix harrumphed several times. "Really,
I cannot tell you how—how much you—well, really
—ah harrumph! Perhaps it can be arranged."

"Oh, Phoenix!" David threw his arms around the bird's neck and then turned a handspring on the grass.

"But for the present, it seems to be getting late," said the Phoenix. "We shall talk it over some other time and decide."

"Golly, it IS late—I hadn't noticed. Well, I'll have to go, or they'll worry about me at home. But may I come up and see you tomorrow?"

"Of course, my boy! In the bustle of morning, in the hush of noon, in the—ah—to be brief, at any time."

"And I'll bring you some cookies, if you like."

"Ah," said the Phoenix, closing its eyes. "Sugar cookies, by any chance?" it asked faintly. David noticed the feathers of its throat jumping up and down with rapid swallowing motions.

"I'll ask my aunt to make some tonight."

"Ah, splendid, my boy! Splendid! Shall we say not more than—ah—that is, not LESS than—ah— fifteen?"

"All right, Phoenix. My aunt keeps a big jar full of cookies, and I can have as many as I like."

The Phoenix took David's arm, and together they strolled to the other end of the ledge.

"Now, don't mention this to anyone, but there is an old goat trail down this side. It is somewhat

grown over, but eyes as sharp as yours should have
no trouble with it. It will make your travels up
and down easier. Another thing—I trust you will
not make known our rendezvous?"

"Our what?"

"You will not tell anyone that I am here?"

"Oh, no. I won't say a word! Well, I'll see you
tomorrow."

"Yes. As the French so cleverly say it—ah—
well, to be brief, good-by, my boy. Until tomorrow,
then."

David waved his hand, found the goat trail, and
started down. He was too happy even to whistle,
so he contented himself with running whenever he
found a level place. And when he reached home, he
stood on his hands in the back yard for two whole
seconds.

2: *In Which It Is Decided
that David Should Have
an Education, and an
Experiment Is Made*

The next day it took less than an hour to reach
the ledge, and David was sure that he could shorten
the time even more when he was familiar with the
goat trail.

The Phoenix was not in sight when he arrived, and for an instant David was stricken with fright. Had the bird gone in spite of its promise? But no— he heard a reassuring noise. It came from the thicket, and it sounded very much like a snore.

David smiled to himself and shouted, "Hello, Phoenix!"

There was a thrashing sound in the thicket, and the Phoenix appeared, looking very rumpled and yawning behind its wing.

"Greetings, my boy!" it cried. "A splendid morning!" Then the Phoenix caught sight of the paper
bag in David's hand and swallowed in a sugges-
tive way.

David thrust the bag of cookies behind his back. "Now, Phoenix," he said firmly, "you have to promise me you won't go away to South America. You said last night that it could be arranged, so let's arrange it right now. Until we do, not one."

The Phoenix drew itself up indignantly. "My very dear fellow," it said, "you wound me. You cut me to the quick. I will not be bribed. I—" It stopped and swallowed again. "Oh, well," it continued, more mildly, "one does not fight fate, does one? I suppose I must accept."

"It's settled, then!" David cried joyfully.

So they sat down on the grass together, and for a long time nothing was heard but sounds of munching.

"My boy," said the Phoenix at last, brushing the crumbs from its chest, "I take a modest pride in my way with words, but nothing in the language can describe these—ah—baked poems. Words fail me."

"I'm glad you like them," David said politely.

"And now, my boy," continued the Phoenix, as it settled back comfortably, "I have been thinking. Yesterday you showed an intelligent interest in my problems and asked intelligent questions. You did not laugh, as others might have done. You have very rare qualities."

David blushed, and mumbled.

"Do not be so modest, my boy! I speak the truth. It came to me that such a mind as yours, having these qualities, should be further cultivated and refined. And I should be avoiding my clear-cut duty if I did not take this task in hand myself. Of course, I suppose some attempt to educate you has already been made, has it not?"

"Well, I go to school, if that's what you mean. Not now, though, because it's summer vacation."

"And what do they teach you there?"

"Oh, reading and writing and arithmetic, and things like that."

"Aha!" said the Phoenix triumphantly. "Just as I feared—a classical education. Understand me—I have nothing against a classical education as such. I realize that Greek and Latin are excellent for the training of the mind. But in the broad view, a classical education is not a true education. Life is real, life is earnest. One must face it with a PRACTICAL education. The problems of Life, my dear fellow!—classical education completely ignores them! For example, how do you tell a true Unicorn from a false one?"

"I—I don't know."

"I thought not. Where do you find the Philosopher's Stone?"

David squirmed uncomfortably. "I'm afraid I don't know that, either," he said in a small voice.

"There you are!" cried the Phoenix. "You do not have a true, practical education—you are not ready for Life. I, my boy, am going to take your education in hand."

"Oh," said David. "Do you mean—are you going to give me—lessons?" Through his mind flashed a picture of the Phoenix (with spectacles on its beak and a ruler in its wing) writing out sentences on a blackboard. The thought gave him a sinking feeling. After all, it was summer—and summer was supposed to be vacation time.

"And what an education it will be!" the Phoenix went on, ignoring his question. "Absolutely without equal! Using to the fullest my vast knowledge, plus a number of trips to—"

"Oh, TRAVELING!" said David, suddenly feeling much better. "That's different. Oh, Phoenix, that'll be wonderful! Where will we go?"

"Everywhere, my boy!" said the Phoenix, with an airy wave of its wing. "To all corners of the earth. We shall visit my friends and acquaintances."

"Oh, do you have—"

"Of course, my boy! I am nothing if not a good mixer. My acquaintances (to mention but a few) include Fauns, Dragons, Unicorns, Trolls, Gryphons, Sea Monsters, Leprechauns, Gnomes, Elves, Nymphs—ah—and many others. All are of the Better Sort, since, as I have many times said, one is known by the company one keeps. And your education will cost you nothing. Of course it WOULD be agreeable if you could supply me with cookies from time to time."

"As many as you want, Phoenix. Will we go to Africa?"

"Naturally, my boy. Your education will include—"

"And Egypt? And China? And Arabia?"

"Yes. Your education will—"

"Oh, Phoenix, Phoenix!" David jumped up and began to dance, while the Phoenix beamed. But suddenly he stopped.

"How are we going to travel, Phoenix?"

"I have wings, my boy."

"Yes, but I don't."

"Do not be so dense, my dear fellow. I shall carry you on my back, of course."

"Oh," said David weakly, "on your—on your back. Are you sure that—isn't there some other— I mean, can you do it?"

The Phoenix drew itself up to its full height. "I am hurt—yes, deeply hurt—by your lack of faith. My magnificent build should make it evident that I am an exceedingly powerful flyer. In my youth I could fly around the world in five hours. But come along. I shall give you proof positive."

David followed the Phoenix to a spot on the edge of the shelf where there was a gap in the bushes. He glanced over the brink. The face of the scarp fell away beneath them, plunging down to the tiny trees and rocks below. He stepped back quickly with a shudder.

"Let's—let's do it tomorrow," he quavered.

"Nonsense," said the Phoenix firmly. "No time like the present. Now, then, up on my back."

"H–h–how am I going to sit?"

"On my back. Quite so—now, your arms around my neck—your legs BEHIND my wings, please— there we are. Ready?"

"No," said David faintly.

"Splendid! The proof is to be demonstrated, the —to be brief, we are off!"

The great wings were outstretched. David gulped, clutched the Phoenix's neck tightly, and shut his eyes. He felt a hopping sensation, then a long, sickening downward swoop that seemed to leave his stomach far behind. A tremendous rush of air snatched at his shirt. He opened his eyes and choked with fright. The ground below was rushing up to meet them, swaying and spinning. Something was terribly wrong. The Phoenix was breathing in hoarse gasps; its wings were pounding the air frantically. Now they had turned back. The scarp loomed before them, solid and blank. Above them —high above them—was the ledge. It looked as though they would not get back to it.

Up . . . up . . . up . . . They crawled through the air. The wings flapped wildly, faster and faster. They were gaining—slipping back—gaining again. The Phoenix sobbed as it stretched its neck in the last effort. Fifty feet . . . twenty feet . . . ten . . . With a tremendous surge of its wings, the Phoenix managed to get one claw over the edge and to seize the branch of a bush in its beak. David's legs

slipped from the bird's back. He dangled from the outstretched neck and prayed. The bush saved them. They scrabbled up over the edge, tottered there for an instant, and dropped on the grass.

For a long time they lay gasping and trembling.

At last the Phoenix weakly raised its head. "Puff—well, my boy—puff, puff—whew!—very narrow squeak. I—puff—"

David could not answer. The earth reeled under him and would not stop no matter how tightly he clutched the grass.

"Puff—I repeat, I am—puff—an exceedingly powerful flyer. There are few birds—none, I dare say—who—puff—could have done even this much. The truth of the matter is that you are a lot— puff—heavier than you look. I hope you are not being overfed at home?"

"I—I don't know," said David, wondering whether or not he was going to be sick.

"Well, my course is clear," said the Phoenix firmly. "I must practice. Setting-up exercises, roadwork, and what not. Diet. Lots of sleep.

Regular hours. Courage, my dear fellow! We shall do it yet!"

And so for the following week the Phoenix practiced.

Every morning David climbed up to the ledge, bringing sandwiches for himself, cookies for the Phoenix, and a wet towel. Then, while he kept count, the Phoenix did setting-up exercises. After this, the bird would jog trot up and down the ledge and practice jumping. Then there would be a fifteen-minute rest and refreshment period. And when that was over, the Phoenix would launch itself into the air. This was the part David liked best. It was a magnificent sight. The Phoenix dashed back and forth at top speed, wheeled in circles, shot straight up like a rocket—plunged, looped—rolled, soared, fluttered. Now and then it would swoop back to the ledge beside David and wipe the sweat from its brow.

"I trust you see signs of progress, my boy?"

David would wrap the wet towel around the Phoenix's neck. "You're doing better and better, Phoenix. I especially like that part where you twist over on your back and loop and plunge, all at the same time."

"I do perform rather well, don't I? It is not easy. But just the thing for (ouch!) muscle tone.

Are there any more cookies? Ah, there are. Delicious! As I was saying, let this be a lesson to you, my boy. If at first you don't succeed, try, try again."

The Phoenix would take wing again. And David would settle back against a rock and watch. Sometimes he thought of the education he was to get. Sometimes he thought how nice it would be if HE could fly. And sometimes he did not think at all, but just sat with his eyes half shut, feeling the sunlight on his face and listening to the wind in the thicket.

At the end of the week the Phoenix, after a brilliant display of acrobatics, landed on the ledge, clasped its wings behind its back, and looked seriously at David.

"Well, my boy," it said, "I believe your education can begin forthwith. Are you ready?"

From the Latin *fatum*, "what is spoken," comes **fate**, "what will be." Greek mythology says that life is controlled by the three goddesses of fate: one who spins the thread of life; one who draws it out; and a third who snips the thread off.

Listening and Thinking

You and your friend Karen are watching TV at her home. The phone rings and Karen gets up to answer it. All you can hear is Karen's part of the conversation. From her replies you can conclude that she is talking to Susan. Karen's replies give you clues to what Susan must be saying.

Read silently what Karen says, watching for the clues. Be prepared to tell what Susan might be saying.

Hello. Karen speaking . . .

Oh, I'm fine, Susan. How are you? . . .

That's too bad. Are you feeling better? . . .

Well, that's good . . .

A week from today? Um-m-m . . . Nothing . . .

For Jan's birthday? That sounds like fun . . .

Oh, it's a good thing you told me. I might have given it away. But how do you expect to keep Jan from finding out? . . .

I hope it works . . .

Emily? She's gone on a trip with her family . . . I'll be glad to call Gail for you . . .

That's all right. I can't visit now either. I'm supposed to clean the basement. Thanks for inviting me. See you next week. Good-by.

Unit Three   The Magic of Language

AL AND THE MAGIC LAMP

Al lived in Paris, Illinois, U.S.A. Maybe if he had lived in Peoria or in Springfield, things would have been different. But he lived in Paris, Illinois, and so this is what happened.

One afternoon Al's dog Snooper came home with an odd-looking copper dish. "Gosh!" said Al. "Where on earth did you dig that up? It looks just like Aladdin's magic lamp in the Arabian Nights stories."

Al took the lamp up to his room and began to wipe off the dirt. Puff! The room was filled with soft smoke. And there, peering down at him, was a huge figure.

"I know who you are!" said Al with delight. "You're a genie. I saw you in a TV cartoon. You were advertising soap."

"I have never advertised anything," said the genie haughtily. "And I'll thank you to keep your animal from sniffing at me like that. I am the Genie of the Lamp. What is your wish?"

"Just a minute," said Al politely. "I don't mean to hurt your feelings, but I'm afraid you might scare my mother."

Then Al closed his door and pulled down the shades. "Now," said Al, "tell me something. How come you're here instead of in Arabia or some place like that?"

"This is Paris," said the genie, "is it not?"

"Yes," said Al. "This is Paris, Illinois, U.S.A."

"Well," said the genie, "my former master told me to take the lamp and meet him in Paris. But there are many cities named Paris, and he didn't say which one. So I selected Paris, Illinois, U.S.A."

"Why?" asked Al. "Why did you choose Paris, Illinois, U.S.A.?"

"Because I wanted a long vacation," said the genie. "I didn't figure that you or your Snooper animal would come and sniff me out. But now you have the lamp, and I will obey your commands."

"All right," said Al. "Let's see what you can do for me." He looked at his messy bedroom and waved his hand at the strings and wires and papers scattered around. "Get all this stuff out of my room," he said.

The genie gave him a pained look. "You mean you want me to do plain housework? Don't you want a solid gold palace or a herd of wild elephants or something like that?"

"Maybe later," said Al. "Right now I want you to get this stuff out of my room—all of it."

"I hear and obey," said the genie. He clapped his hands once—and the room was absolutely bare of furniture. Everything was gone, even the bed.

"Oh, my gosh!" said Al. "I guess I didn't really mean all of it. Please put everything back the way it was."

In an instant everything was back. But now the bedroom looked even a little messier than before.

"That didn't work out so well," said Al. "I'll try you on something else. Snooper and I are hungry. Bring us two nice hot dogs on buns."

"I hear and obey," said the genie. He clapped his hands again—and there, standing on buns, were two cute puppies. But they were so hot that they waved little fans to keep cool.

"For Pete's sake," said Al. "Take the poor things back and make them comfortable right away."

The puppies immediately disappeared and so did the genie. Then Al flopped on his bed and began to think hard. What sort of task can you give to a genie who thinks that "hot dog" means "warm puppy?"

Suddenly Al heard the most awful screeching under his window. He jumped from the bed and looked out. What excitement! Boys were running to his house from all directions. And in front of his house was a huge fire truck.

"We're on fire!" thought Al, as he started for the door. But just then the firemen rushed into his room, followed by his frightened mother.

"Thank heavens you're safe!" said Mother. "Neighbor Fidget called the fire department when

he saw smoke coming from under your window shades."

"Oh," said Al with relief. "That smoke was nothing to worry about. It came from my magic lamp."

"A magic lamp!" said a startled fireman. "Let me see it. We have to be sure it's not dangerous."

"This is it," thought Al. "He'll accidentally rub the lamp, the genie will pop out, and my mother will really be scared."

But the fireman didn't rub the lamp at all. To him it was just an odd-looking copper dish. So he merely checked to see that it had no flame, and then he put the lamp down again.

Meanwhile Al's mother was getting more and more embarrassed.

"Please don't take this magic-lamp business seriously," she said. "Al is always experimenting with something. Yesterday he made a clock without hands for people who don't care what time it is."

The firemen looked over at the clock and laughed. "I see what you mean," said one, and he rumpled Al's hair. "That's one clock that will never show the wrong time." And when Al looked at his clock with no hands, he had to laugh, too. It did seem kind of silly, after all.

Mother took the firemen downstairs, apologizing all the way. Then Al watched the fire truck drive off and saw the boys drifting down the street. And seeing the boys reminded Al that he had better not waste any more time. His baseball team had a big game scheduled, and he had to get there right away. Maybe he could use the genie during the game.

Al carefully closed his windows so that no more smoke would pour through. Then he called the genie.

"Do you know what a bat is?" asked Al.

"Yes, master," said the genie. "I do."

"Can you make a magic bat?" asked Al.

"Of course I can," said the genie. "Magic is my specialty."

"Okay," said Al. "Stay inside the lamp. And when you hear me say NOW, you must at once give me a magic bat."

"I hear and obey," said the genie.

Then Al put the lamp in a shopping bag and carried it off to the ball field.

For the first few innings Al didn't see a good opportunity to make use of the genie. And then his chance came. With the score tied and the bases loaded, two boys struck out and it was his turn at bat. So Al took a firm grip and smiled confidently. "NOW!" he said.

And everyone on both teams screeched at the same time. There, swooping down over home plate,

was a huge flying bat. Its giant wings cast a shadow over the field.

Snooper began to jump into the air, trying to scare the bat away. But the players scattered like leaves in a windstorm. Some crawled into the thick bushes, others crouched under the steps of a house, and the rest hid behind a large billboard.

Quickly Al called the genie out of the lamp.

"Take that bat away!" he yelled. "Don't you know the difference between a baseball bat and a

living one? I think that you're making all those
mistakes on purpose."

The genie smiled. "I only hear and obey," he
said.

The bat disappeared, the genie sank back into
the lamp, and the boys came drifting back. They
were afraid to come too close, but just stood around,
staring respectfully at the lamp. Then someone
yelled to them from the top of the billboard. Al
looked up and saw his best friend, Kenny.

"Come on down," called Al. "It's safe now."

"I can't!" yelled Kenny. "My pants are stuck on a nail! I can't get loose!"

"Just a minute," said Al. And he hurried to rub the lamp. "Get my friend down here, safe and sound," he ordered the genie.

"I hear and obey," said the genie. He clapped his hands, and there stood Kenny before them. But the boys gave one look and started to laugh. The genie had taken Kenny right out of his trousers. The pants were still stuck on the nail at the top of the billboard.

"Holy cow!" said Al to the genie. "Put his pants on!"

In an instant the genie was wearing Kenny's pants. They were such a tight fit and the genie looked so ridiculous that even Al and Kenny had to laugh.

"Cut that out!" said Al. And he saw the genie wave a huge pair of shears, ready to cut the pants.

Then Al seized the lamp. "Stop!" he yelled. "Don't cut anything! Just put the pants back on Kenny!"

And at last Kenny was properly dressed again.

"Golly," said Kenny. "Your genie is even better than the ones on TV. Tell him to make us rich. Make him give us a pile of dollar bills."

"I'll do better than that," said Al grandly. And to the genie he said, "Get each of us a big pile of ten dollar bills. Make sure they're good ones, not counterfeit."

"I hear and obey," said the genie. He clapped his hands. And in front of each boy appeared a large pile of ten dollar bills.

The boys could hardly believe their eyes. They flopped down in the grass and began to count the money greedily. For a few moments there was no sound but the eager rustling of bills.

Then a shrill sound filled the air—the wailing of police sirens. Frightened, the boys peered through the bushes. And they heard two policemen talking.

"Yes," said one of the policemen, "I just heard about it. Someone stole all the ten dollar bills from every bank in town. The FBI has the serial numbers of all the stolen bills. Anyone who tries to spend that money might find himself in jail."

The boys looked at each other fearfully. Then they began to dump all the money in front of Al.

"You and your genie!" said Kenny. "First you wanted to win the game by cheating with a magic bat. Now your genie tries to give us stolen money. You're both nothing but crooks!"

"I didn't know this money was stolen," said Al. "And the magic bat was just a joke." But the boys wouldn't listen to him, and they all left.

Al ordered the genie to return the money to the banks. He wanted to walk away and leave the lamp right there in the bushes, but he was afraid that somebody else might find it and get into trouble. So he put the lamp back into the shopping bag and started for home.

For the rest of the day Al was so upset with the genie that he didn't talk to him at all. But then, as Al was in bed, he thought he would be friendly again and give the genie an easy job. So he rubbed the lamp and said, "Put out the light, please."

The light went out promptly, and Al settled back to sleep. Then a thought struck him. How come he hadn't heard the click of the light switch when the light went out?

Al got up and used his flashlight. Yes, the genie had put out the light all right. He had put the entire light fixture out on the street. Even the wall switch was gone.

"Bring the light inside again," ordered Al. And to himself he thought, "This is the end. Tomorrow I'll get rid of the lamp and the genie that goes with it."

He spent a restless night. In the morning, as he reached for his schoolbooks, Al remembered something awful. He had forgotten about his homework. A written composition about the discovery of America was due today, and he hadn't even started it. There was only one thing to do. He would have to use the genie.

Al rubbed the lamp, and the genie appeared with his usual question: "What is your wish?"

"Do you know all about Christopher Columbus and the discovery of America?" asked Al.

"Yes, I do," said the genie.

"Well," said Al, "write me two or three pages about it and put the papers on my desk in school. But remember, everything you write must be true; I want no mistakes this time."

"I hear and obey," said the genie.

Al ran most of the way to school and came into the room just in time to see the class monitor collecting the homework papers from the top of his desk. "Gosh," thought Al, "I didn't even get a chance to look at them. I hope nothing is wrong with my homework."

Apparently something was wrong, because the teacher frowned at Al's papers and put them in an envelope.

"Albert," said the teacher, "I don't think you should make such a joke of your schoolwork. I'm sending your papers to the office, and I'm sure the principal will want to see you about them."

"What has that genie done now?" Al wondered. All through the next lesson he found it hard to keep his mind on his work. And his heart sank as he saw a messenger come in with a note from the principal. Sure enough, he was wanted in the office.

The principal was studying the homework papers as Al entered. "Did I do the work wrong?" asked Al timidly.

"Well," said the principal, "neither I nor anyone else in this whole school would know whether your papers are right or wrong. Tell me, Albert, what made you decide to do all your homework in Arabic?"

Arabic? Al was disgusted with himself. Why hadn't he thought of warning the genie to write in English? The only thing left to do was to tell the truth. So Al told the whole story, from beginning to end.

"Albert," said the principal, "the newspapers say that the banks just misplaced those ten dollar bills and then found them again. You're letting your imagination run away with you. But if you think you do have Aladdin's magic lamp, suppose you just return it and do your homework in English from now on."

"Yes, sir," said Al. "That genie has brought me nothing but trouble. Because of him my best friends are mad at me. I'll get rid of the lamp right away."

As soon as Al got home, he went to his room and rubbed the lamp.

"What is your wish?" asked the genie.

"My wish is this," said Al. "And listen carefully, because if you make any more mistakes you'll spend the rest of your life emptying all the oceans with a teaspoon."

"I listen, master," said the genie. "What is your wish?"

"Take your lamp," said Al. "Go to Paris, France, and never, never come back here again!"

The genie gave a terrible frown. But he had to obey. With a puff of black smoke he disappeared forever.

Then Al went out to find Snooper, and to his surprise he saw his dog playing with an odd-looking ring.

"Gosh!" said Al. "It looks just like the magic wishing ring that Aladdin had in the Arabian Nights stories."

Al took the ring up to his room and began to wipe off the dirt. Puff! The room was filled with soft smoke. And there, peering down at him, was a huge genie.

Snooper growled. With dismay he saw Al close the door and pull down the shades. Then the dog sank to the floor and covered his head with his paws.

"BONES AND BISCUITS! HERE WE GO AGAIN!"

Would you believe that our word **sun** is related to the Latin word for sun, *sol*? Both come from the same parent word, which began with an *s* and a vowel. When the parent word was the subject in a sentence, it ended with an *l*. Otherwise it ended with an *n*.

WHY THE ANIMALS DO NOT TALK

This short play is based on an Iroquoian legend. It may be given as a reading with the characters seated or standing in a half circle and the narrators standing to either side.

CHARACTERS

FIRST NARRATOR	BEAR
SECOND NARRATOR	PANTHER
WOLF	RACCOON
BEAVER	FOX
HORSE	GREAT SPIRIT
DOG	

FIRST NARRATOR. Long before the white man came to the Americas, long, long ago, animals had the gift of speech. Then not only red men sat around great fires burning late into the night when important things had to be decided. The panther, the bear, the fox, the wolf, the beaver —all the animals were there too, speaking their thoughts as clearly as the men. For in the beginning, the Great Spirit in the sky made animals and men like brothers.

SECOND NARRATOR. In those long ago days, animals and men helped one another. The beaver showed the Indians how to build their houses snug and warm. The bear and the wolf told them how to follow a trail through the forest. The dog taught them his patience and loyalty. From the raccoon, the red men learned how to climb the tallest trees. The horse taught them how to run, and the panther how to hide and spring forth from the hiding place like a burst of wind. Last of all, the fox taught men to be sly and clever.

FIRST NARRATOR. Thus, for many summers and winters, men and animals lived in peace and happiness. The Great Spirit was pleased. But the time came when the animals knew they had taught the Indians too much. The wolf called a secret council, and he was the first to speak as all the animals sat around the council fire.

WOLF. Brothers, I have called this council to warn you that we are in danger. We have taught the Indians all we know. Now they are more skilled in the ways of the forest than we are.

BEAVER. (*Anxiously*) It is true. The houses of the Indians are even better than my own. They cut trees as I showed them and make houses with mud between the logs to keep out the wind and snow of winter. Now they cut trees and make canoes of them. They have learned to make paddles from wood. With knives in their hands, they can do what my sharp teeth will never do.

HORSE. I, too, have found that I can no longer run races with men. I have taught them to run more swiftly than I. Now, I only stand quietly watching when they have races on the plains. But I am not jealous. The Great Spirit is pleased that men and animals are friends.

DOG. The horse is right. It was the wish of the Great Spirit that we teach men our skills. I do not complain even though I have found that men now have more patience than I. Sometimes I fall asleep when I should be on watch by the campfire at night, but men will wait and watch for many suns and never weary. Yet, I do my best. And when the long watch is over, I play with the boys and girls. Man is my brother and I love him. I think the wolf was wrong to call this council without telling the Indians about it.

BEAR. It would be more honest to meet the Indians face to face. I too am sorry that I taught them to follow the trail so well. Often when I hunt with them, I lose the scent, but they follow the trail deep into the forest.

PANTHER. (*Snarling*) Why should we not be jealous of men? Why should we trust them? I can hide to spring upon my prey better than any of you. But the other day, when I used the greatest skill I have in hiding, a man parted the branches and laughed in my face because he had found me so easily. I wanted to bite him and claw him for laughing at me.

RACCOON. Panther, you are too fierce. You know how it would anger the Great Spirit if he heard your words. Yet, I too have to admit that the wolf is right. Sometimes I am afraid of men, and I wonder how I could escape if they tried to hunt me. I taught them to climb so well that the Indian boys dare to climb higher than I. They climb to where the branches are so thin that they sway this way and that, far above the ground.

FOX. It was not clever of us to teach all we know to man. I am ashamed to think I was not more clever, for I am the slyest of all animals. I should have known that the time would come when men would be as sly as I am. Sometimes I think that men can trick others even better than I.

BEAR. I don't see why anyone should be proud of being tricky, but I suppose that is the way the Great Spirit made you, Fox. You can't help it. I am sorry to hear that you think men are even better than you at tricking others. I am bigger than man and I would never be afraid of him in a fair fight. But it may be that he will be able to harm me by being more sly than I am.

WOLF. Listen everyone! I called this council because we are all in danger. There is a danger none of you has thought about. Do you know the red man would like to use your skins to keep warm in winter?

RACCOON. (*Worriedly*) Wolf, that is a terrible thought! Yet, when I was hiding in a tree the other day, I saw a man and his squaw looking at a beaver. The Indian told her they needed something for keeping their baby warm in winter. I do not like the way he eyed the beaver's thick coat.

BEAVER. (*Shouting angrily*) And after all I've done for the Indians! The fox is right. I'm sorry now that I ever taught them to cut down trees and to build houses.

WOLF. I always hide my little ones from the red man since I heard a brave promise a girl that if she would marry him he would make her a bed of wolfskins, with a bearskin for a blanket.

BEAR. If man can think such evil thoughts, I can never be his friend again.

PANTHER. Let us unite and drive him from the forest forever.

FOX. We must think of a clever way to do it.

HORSE. You will anger the Great Spirit. He loves man as he loves us all.

PANTHER. (*Snarling*) If the Great Spirit won't protect us from the Indians, then we have a right to get rid of them.

WOLF. If we all fight together, we can rush into the villages and kill every man, woman, and child.

BEAR. I think it's unfair to rush in without warning. I think we should challenge the Indians to an open fight. We are still stronger and more numerous than they are and would defeat them.

BEAVER. I know a safer way. When winter comes, we can tear down their houses while they sleep. If they get cold enough, they might promise to treat us as equals.

HORSE. I will never agree to harming the Indians. If you must get rid of them, invite them on a long hunt. Lead them to the land over the mountains, then steal back to your homes.

PANTHER. Do you think they could not return as well as you can? Your plan and the beaver's are too kind. Only by killing every one of them will we ever be safe.

FOX. I can teach you all how to cheat and steal while pretending to be friendly. You must admit slyness is better than bloodshed. Strip the corn from its stalks. Steal everything the Indians have planted. Steal their canoes so that they cannot travel on the river. Then they will starve and never know we are their enemies.

DOG. (*Sadly*) For the first time in my life, I am ashamed to be a beast. How many times have men nursed us when we were sick, taken us into their houses when we were cold, fed us when we were hungry? Instead of killing the Indians, how much wiser it would be to ask them to teach us as we taught them. Then all the animals would be as skilled as man is now.

PANTHER. (*Sneering*) Your friendship with men has made you a coward, Dog. You have lived so long with them that you no longer deserve the name of beast!

WOLF. Dog will tell what we have said. We should never have asked him to come to this council.

PANTHER. Dog, you are a coward! You have sold yourself to men for a few pieces of left-over food, for the petting of the Indian boys and girls.

HORSE. (*Angrily*) You have spoken cruel words to my friend the dog. I will leave this council, and the dog and I will fight against you with the Indians.

FIRST NARRATOR. Suddenly thunder roared across the sky and all of the animals trembled.

GREAT SPIRIT. I have heard your words. I have left my home in the sky to come to this council. I am not pleased that you cannot live in peace with man. Because of your follies, I must change my plan. I wished all my creatures to live happily together. Since you will not, I now take from you the gift of speech. You shall never again hold a council like this one. You will be without words, and men will no longer speak with you.

I will tell man that henceforth he may hunt the panther and the wolf. He may kill them in any way he wishes. The bear he will fight openly and honestly, for that is how the bear wishes to fight. I will tell the red man that he may take the fur of the beaver and raccoon to warm his children. The fox is a thief. The Indian will set traps for him and use his skin for clothing too. The horse and dog are guilty only of coming to this council. Man will continue to befriend them. He will speak only a few words to them, and they will be unable to answer him.

SECOND NARRATOR. And so it was. The panther, the wolf, and the bear became enemies of man, whereas the horse and the dog remained his friends. And so it was that all the animals lost the gift of speech.

In medieval times a man was complimented if he was said to be *sleih,* for in Middle English it meant "clever or skillful." But to say that a man is **sly** today is to insult him, for the word now means "the ability to get what one wants through trickery."

All Five Senses

A good writer uses descriptions which help his reader form clear sensory images. The reader can imagine the smells, tastes, sights, sounds, and touch of the things being described. In other words, a writer tries to appeal not only to the "mind's eye," but to the "mind's nose, fingers, tongue, and ears!"

The writer of the sketch on pages 78-79 chose images which appeal only to the reader's sense of sight. He made no attempt to describe the crunch of the ski poles poking through the snow's crust or the swish and grind of the ski's steel edges cutting into the snow as Ken christied to a stop. Nor did he try to describe the bite of the wind on Ken's cheeks, the warmth of the sun on his back. He never mentioned the smell of the spruces or the taste of dryness in Ken's mouth.

Had these images been included, would your mental picture have been more complete?

Using words which will help your reader form good sensory images, write a paragraph describing any experience you wish. These suggestions may help.

1. Walking in the woods on a fall day
2. Being stalled in a traffic jam on a hot afternoon
3. Going Christmas shopping

THE LANGUAGE OF SYMBOLS

Do the above pictures remind you of anything? Each of them is called a symbol because each one stands for or represents something else. For example, a picture of a lion may symbolize the idea of courage. What ideas are represented by the pictures at the top of this page?

A symbol helps to get an idea across. It may be called by different names, but it is still a symbol.

Letters of our alphabet are symbols for the sounds of our language. These letters are combined to form written words, which are the symbols for spoken words.

Numerals are symbols used to write or record numbers.

Symbols for whole words are called abbreviations.

Emblems are used by many nations and clubs as symbols of the ideas for which they stand. Sometimes an emblem is worn in the form of a badge to indicate a person's membership, position, or rank in a certain group.

Cattle brands and rubber stamps may be used as symbols of ownership.

In the Middle Ages kings and kingdoms had coats of arms and crests. At first these symbolized a quality such as courage, or an incident in the owner's life. Later they came to indicate the family or country from which a person came.

A flag is another form of symbol and may stand for a country, a state, a city, or an organization.

Trademarks were originally used by craftsmen of the Middle Ages as a guarantee of fine workmanship. Today many companies use trademarks—symbols put on products to identify the manufacturers. Here is the trademark of the publisher of this book.

1817

The seal, long used by individuals and nations on official papers, is a symbol.

In the Middle Ages few people could write, yet a signature often was needed. A design—usually the same as appeared on the coat of arms—was cut into a wood or metal block. Papers could be signed by pressing the design, called a seal, into a spot of warm wax dropped onto the paper. Sometimes kings and other officials used their signet rings to press a design into the warm wax.

Seals are still used today, although the method of applying them has changed. This is the seal of the United States government.

Symbols were used in still another way on English store signs in the 1700's. Since most people of that time could not read, a printed sign was of little value to a shopkeeper. He needed a sign that would picture what he sold in his store. Even today, although our language continues to grow, many people still use signs to picture what they sell in their shops.

As we have seen, a symbol may have many names. We may know it by such words as picture, letter, numeral, abbreviation, badge, brand, stamp, emblem, coat of arms, crest, flag, trademark, seal, sign. And there are others. Symbols are everywhere. Walk through a store, leaf through a magazine, watch television and outdoor advertising. You will see that we are surrounded by symbols.

---

1. Study the illustration on page 194. Compare the symbols used as store signs in the 1700's with those you see today. Which of the symbols shown on page 194 are still used as part of store signs? Which ones are now out-of-date?

2. Consult reference books for information about traffic signs used on our highways. Then make a chart or notebook that includes the road signs that use *only* symbols.

3. Imagine that as a member of the Federal Highway Administration you have been assigned the task of changing the road signs. You are to replace the words with pictorial signs that can be easily understood. What types of symbols would you use?

4. Imagine a make-believe country with you as its owner. Name your country and then draw a map that uses symbols to indicate its capital, bodies of water, important cities, mountain regions, and other important places.

IT'S AN OLD STORY!

For over two thousand years people have enjoyed hearing and repeating fables. A fable is a story whose characters are animals that talk, think, and act very much the way humans do. This type of story is used to teach a particular lesson. In the following three fables, a lion is one of the important characters.

The Lion and the Mouse

One day while a lion was sleeping, a mischievous little mouse dared to jump right up on him and start dancing. Startled, the lion awoke, placed his huge paw upon the mouse, and opened wide his big jaws so he could swallow the little creature.

"Oh, King of the Beasts," cried the mouse, "please forgive me this time and spare my life! I will gladly make it up to you by helping you sometime."

The lion was so amused at the idea of the mouse being able to help him, that he set the mouse free.

A while later, the lion was trapped in a hunter's net. Although he tried with all his might, he was not able to free himself. Just then the little mouse came along, and seeing the lion's predicament, immediately started gnawing away at the ropes that bound the King of Beasts. One by one the ropes loosened, and the lion finally broke through his bonds.

"Wasn't I right?" said the mouse.

The Gnat and the Lion

A gnat flitted up to a lion and declared, "You think you're more powerful than I am, don't you? Well, you are very wrong! Just what kind of strength do you have? You scratch and bite just the way peasants fight. I'm much stronger than you. I'll show you! Come on, let's have a fight!"

While the gnat daringly proceeded to sting the lion on his nose and cheeks, the lion lunged and roared. However, the lion's face became scratched and clawed until it finally bled. Completely exhausted and suffering great discomfort, the lion slumped onto the ground.

Bursting with pride, the gnat soared away—right into a spider's web in which it became entangled.

As the gnat realized its doom, it thought, "I overpowered a lion, King of Beasts, but now, here I am trapped by a wretched spider!"

The Lion and the Bulls

Once there were four powerful bulls who were very good friends and grazed together in a lush, green meadow. But a much-feared lion who also dwelled in this territory was anxious to devour them. The lion realized, though, that as long as the bulls remained together, he would never get an opportunity to attack them. And he also knew that he would greatly endanger his own life if he *did* attempt a frontal attack.

Consequently the lion's only choice was to use his wits rather than his strength. He began by secretly telling each bull that his companions were very treacherous. One by one, each bull became suspicious of the other. The lion continued this plan until all the bulls were angry with each other and no longer trusted one another. Soon they were quarreling and fighting, and their fury knew no bounds. And so the lion attacked each bull separately and thus devoured the once inseparable friends.

Key Words in Sentences

The Arabian camel has one hump and the Bactrian camel of southern Asia has two. If you had to check the accuracy of this statement, what books would you use?

A reference book, probably an encyclopedia, would be your most available source of information. But before you can check this statement in a reference book you will have to decide which heading to look under. To do this you will need to locate the key word (or words) in the sentence. What heading would you look under?

Read the following sentences and locate the key words in each. Check the accuracy of your answers by using reference books.

1. Athens, Greece, was the site of the first Olympic games held in modern times.
2. Hippocrates, an ancient Greek physician, is called "The Father of Medicine."
3. Salt is known chemically as sodium chloride.
4. A symphony orchestra has four sections: woodwind, string, brass, and percussion.
5. Alaska became the forty-ninth state of the Union in 1959.
6. Zebulon Pike, for whom Colorado's Pikes Peak is named, was an American explorer.

HELEN KELLER

Even after my illness I remembered one of the words I had learned in these early months. It was the word "water," and I continued to make some sound for that word after all other speech was lost. I ceased making the sound "wah-wah" only when I learned to spell the word.

My hands felt every object and observed every motion, and in this way I learned to know many things. Soon I felt the need of some communication with others and began to make crude signs. A shake of the head meant "No" and a nod, "Yes," a pull meant "Come" and a push, "Go." Was it bread that I wanted? Then I would imitate the acts of cutting the slices and buttering them. If I wanted my mother to make ice cream for dinner I made the sign for working the freezer and shivered, indicating cold. My mother, moreover, succeeded in making me understand a good deal. I always knew when she wished me to bring her something, and I would run upstairs or anywhere else she indicated. Indeed, I owe to her loving wisdom all that was bright and good in my long night.

I understood a good deal of what was going on about me. At five I learned to fold and put away the clean clothes when they were brought in from the laundry, and I distinguished my own from the rest. I knew by the way my mother and aunt dressed when they were going out, and I invariably begged to go with them. I was always sent for when there was company, and when the guests took their leave, I waved my hand to them, I think with a vague remembrance of the meaning of the gesture.

I do not remember when I first realized that I was different from other people; but I knew it before my teacher came to me. I had noticed that my mother and my friends did not use signs as I did when they wanted anything done, but talked with their mouths. Sometimes I stood between two persons who were conversing and touched their lips. I could not understand, and was vexed. I moved my lips and gesticulated frantically without result. This made me so angry at times that I kicked and screamed until I was exhausted.

I felt as if invisible hands were holding me, and I made frantic efforts to free myself. I struggled, not that struggling helped matters, but the spirit of resistance was strong within me; I generally broke down in tears and physical exhaustion.

My parents were deeply grieved and perplexed. We lived a long way from any school for the blind or the deaf, and it seemed unlikely that anyone would come to such an out-of-the-way place as Tuscumbia to teach a child who was both deaf and blind. Indeed my friends and relatives sometimes doubted whether I could be taught.

But finally, with the help of many people including Alexander Graham Bell, a teacher was found.

The most important day I remember in all my life is the one on which my teacher, Anne Mansfield Sullivan, came to me. I am filled with wonder when I consider the immeasurable contrasts between the two lives which it connects. It was the third of March, 1887, three months before I was seven years old.

The morning after my teacher came she led me into her room and gave me a doll. When I had played with it a little while, Miss Sullivan slowly spelled into my hand the word "d-o-l-l." I was at once interested in this finger play and tried to imitate it. When I finally succeeded in making the letters correctly I was flushed with childish pleasure and pride. Running downstairs to my mother I held up my hand and made the letters for doll. I did not know that I was spelling a word or even that words existed; I was simply making my fingers go in monkey-like imitation. In the days that followed I learned to spell in this uncomprehending way a great many words, among them *pin, hat, cup* and a few verbs like *sit, stand,* and *walk.* But my teacher had been with me several weeks before I understood that everything has a name.

One day, while I was playing with my new doll, Miss Sullivan put my big rag doll into my lap also, spelled "d-o-l-l," and tried to make me understand that "d-o-l-l" applied to both. Earlier in the day we had a tussle over the words "m-u-g" and "w-a-t-e-r." Miss Sullivan had tried to impress it upon me that "m-u-g" is *mug* and "w-a-t-e-r" is *water,* but I persisted in confounding the two. In despair she had dropped the subject for the time, only to renew it at the first opportunity.

We walked down the path to the well-house, attracted by the fragrance of the honeysuckle with which it was covered. Someone was drawing water and my teacher placed my hand under the spout. As the cool stream gushed over one hand she spelled into the other the word *water*, first slowly, then rapidly. I stood still, my whole attention fixed upon the motions of her fingers. Suddenly I felt a misty consciousness as of something forgotten —a thrill of returning thought; and somehow the mystery of language was revealed to me. I knew then that "w-a-t-e-r" meant the wonderful cool something that was flowing over my hand. That living word awakened my soul, gave it light, hope,

joy, set it free! There were barriers still, it is true, but barriers that could in time be swept away.

I left the well-house eager to learn. Everything had a name, and each name gave birth to a new thought. As we returned to the house every object which I touched seemed to quiver with life. That was because I saw everything with the strange, new sight that had come to me.

I had now the key to all language, and I was eager to learn to use it. Children who hear acquire language without any particular effort; the words that fall from others' lips they catch on the wing, as it were, delightedly, while the little deaf child must trap them by a slow and often painful process. But whatever the process, the result is wonderful.

---

1. Helen Keller was born on June 27, 1880, but she often spoke of March 3, 1887, as her real "birthday." What do you think she meant by this?

2. How would you describe Miss Sullivan?

3. Miss Sullivan was blind at one time but recovered some of her eyesight through an operation. How would this help to make her a good teacher for Helen Keller?

Getting Help from Illustrations

Illustrations serve many important purposes.

Turn to page 23 of "All-Around Athlete." The illustration on this page *sets the scene* for the story, giving the reader a picture of the era and the action which is about to take place.

The illustrations on pages 26-27 of the same selection are *informative*. Readers familiar with track and field events will note that the style for the high jump has changed since 1932. The other illustrations may help some readers learn what the shot, javelin, and discus are.

The illustrations for "Champions Don't Cry," pages 55-76, *dramatize a situtation*. How does the picture on page 65 dramatize what is happening?

Some illustrations, like the stories they accompany, are *entertaining*. Can you name a story which has this kind of illustrations?

Occasionally an illustration is simply *decorative*. The cock on page 22 is such an illustration.

Some illustrations serve more than one purpose. Turn to page 158. Which of the above purposes does this illustration fulfill?

Find "Monsters of Myth and Legend" in the Table of Contents. Turn to the story and discuss the purpose of each illustration. Choose at least four other selections you have read and do the same.

TWO KINDS OF TALK

There were four separate classes in the Willow-brook school and the one you went into depended on how old you were. Matthew went with the five and six year olds, Sister with the sevens and eights, and Roosevelt with the nines, tens, elevens. Manowar showed up in this class, too. And then there was one for the big boys and girls, twelve and up, only this one didn't have many pupils in it except on rainy days.

Roosevelt's class wasn't ready yet for putting into, but on the blackboard, Mrs. Dinwiddie showed him privately how to fix up the left-over number.

"You make a little shelf," she explained, "like this: —————. You put something underneath it to hold it up. Like this: $\dfrac{}{3}$. Then on top you set

the left-over number. Like this: $\dfrac{2}{3}$.

"There. See? The left-over number can rest safe and comfortable while you're waiting to need it. How's that?"

"Good," said Roosevelt. "It's a good idea. I wonder why I didn't think of doing that myself."

Mrs. Dinwiddie had no stick. She did not look teachery. Too young, for one thing. Too small, for another. She had cornsilk hair and if she hadn't worn shoes with spiky heels, she wouldn't have been much taller than Roosevelt. Her sweater and her skirt were both sky blue and she kept pushing her sweater sleeves up above her elbows. When she walked around the room, her high heels went *click-click-click* on the floor so you knew where she was whether you were looking that way or not.

Lulubelle Clay, the slow bean-picker, saw she was different, too.

"Mrs. Dinwiddie," asked Lulubelle, "are you a real teacher?"

"Yes, Lulubelle, I am," Mrs. Dinwiddie answered. "At least I'm a teacher. Are you real, Lulubelle?

If you're real, then I'm real, too." She held out her arm. "Here. Pinch." The class held its breath. Lulubelle pinched. "How about it? Am I real?"

"Yes," said Lulubelle. "You're real."

"Tell me, Lulubelle, why did you think maybe I wasn't real?"

"I don't know," said Lulubelle, "only most generally the teacher has a stick and she whips me to make me read." Lulubelle grinned. "I still can't read."

"We'll fix that," said Mrs. Dinwiddie. "Reading is nothing else but understanding talk through your eyes instead of through your ears. It's not so hard."

Mrs. Dinwiddie was great on stories. How you tell if a story is good, she said, is if people keep quiet and listen while you tell it to them. If the story is good enough, you don't have to tell them to keep still. They won't remember to wiggle; they'll be too interested. A story doesn't have to be true. It may be true or it may not be true—it's nice to know which—but what's important is, does the audience like it. Audience. They're the people you want to get to listen to your story. Or to read it, once you get it written down. Writing is nothing else but talk written down.

Everyone in the class had a chance to tell a story. Roosevelt called his, "My Brother Matthew." He made it true because he wasn't so good at inventing stories. He told about old Matthew and his jokes and how he bumped his head a-purpose on the attic roof and how he was always finding something interesting everywhere he went and especially about him crawling around the junk pile at Quimby's Quarters and coming up with a beat-up old harmonica that squawked. The boys and girls liked this story quite well. Anyway they listened without a wiggle, and at the end, they laughed and clapped their hands.

When Manowar's turn came, he stood up and announced: "Mine's a whopper."

His story took off something like Jack and the Beanstalk. He told about a boy named Joshway, who found an old tomato can and filled it with dirt and planted a sunflower seed in it. At least it looked to Joshway like a sunflower seed, but later on, he was not so sure. Joshway watered the dirt every day and after a while the seed sprouted and then it grew very fast and very big. Some days it grew as much as a foot before lunch.

Wherever Joshway went, from one ripe crop to another, he toted his plant along, from carrots to onions to cauliflower and so on. Finally the plant got as tall as a telephone pole, and it grew such fine spready branches that Joshway built a platform high up on a couple of the branches and fixed himself a small house among the shiny green leaves.

One day a pair of catbirds flew in and asked him if he minded if they built themselves a nest in his tree. On the opposite side from his own house, of course, they explained. Joshway decided he'd let them do it, thinking if they weren't too close, he might enjoy their company.

Another day he woke up in the morning and found a possum hanging from a branch by its tail. The possum didn't ask permission. He stayed on without a by-your-leave and he was no bother to Joshway because he appeared not to do anything ever except sleep.

All this time the tree was growing at the bottom too. Tough snaky roots broke through the tomato can and split it all to pieces and they crept down into the ground. These roots did their growing at night mostly. Every morning Joshway would pull them out of the ground, and every night the roots would go back down in, each time a little deeper. Came a morning when Joshway found he couldn't pull them out. They were stuck fast. It was time to move on to another crop, but he couldn't leave the tree behind and his house and all. So there was nothing for it but he had to stay and live there in his tree house. He got rather hungry, not having any work, but by

and by folks took to coming along and wanting to pay
rent for branches to build houses on for themselves.
Pretty soon Joshway had every pocket full of paper
money and he had enough people living in his tree
to make two sides for a softball game.

Here Manowar stopped talking and walked over to the drinking fountain and took a good long gulp.

"Is that the end?" asked Lulubelle.

"No," said Manowar, coming back from the fountain. "A bulldozer came rolling along and a cat was driving it. A big fierce cat he was, black-and-yellow stripes and extra-long whiskers. The cat said, 'I'll give you five minutes to move out, and then I'm going to run right over your tree, houses and all.'

"Joshway had to think fast. He thought for three minutes. Then he whispered something to the cat-birds and that took another minute. The birds bobbed their heads and chirped and fluttered their wings. Then he whispered something to the possum, who kept his eyes shut and gave no more sign of life than he ever had.

"Right then the cat decided the five minutes were up. He started the bulldozer bearing down on the tree.

" 'Go,' Joshway shouted, and the catbirds flew straight at the bulldozer, and the cat jumped up in the air to catch them and their feathers flew. The possum leaped down from his branch and coiled his tail around the steering wheel. The bulldozer slipped sideways and scraped past the tree, taking only a small chip out of its trunk. Faster and faster went the bulldozer, the possum still hanging on and the cat racing after it until they were all clean out of sight.

"Joshway breathed long and deep.

" 'The possum doesn't worry me,' he said. 'He can look after himself. It's too bad about the catbirds, though. I'll miss having them around.'

"And right then he heard, 'Meow, meow,' and he looked up and there were the catbirds sitting on their nest with their breasts all swelled up looking as though they'd swallowed the bulldozer.

" 'Hi,' said Joshway. 'Glad you made it back. Great job you did. Much obliged.' He climbed up into his tree house and sat down and began to eat his lunch. 'I guess I was wrong,' he said to himself.

" 'Wrong about what?' the catbirds asked, both at once, expecting more praise.

" 'Wrong about that seed I planted in the tomato can,' said Joshway. 'I guess it couldn't have been a sunflower seed, after all.' "

When you sit in an **audience,** you wait to see or hear someone or something. The Latin *audire* means "to hear." At one time the word audience was commonly used to refer to a gathering before a king or other person of high rank.

April Rain Song

Let the rain kiss you.
Let the rain beat upon your head with silver
    liquid drops.
Let the rain sing you a lullaby.

The rain makes still pools on the sidewalk.
The rain makes running pools in the gutter.
The rain plays a little sleep-song on our roof
    at night—

And I love the rain.

218

Unit Four   Rivers and Roads

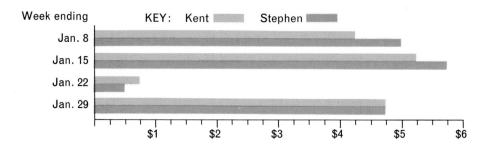

More Help from Illustrations

Some information is more easily understood when illustrated with a map, graph, chart, or table. For example, to write the information given by the bar graph at the top of this page would require many paragraphs. The graph shows how much money two boys earned over a four-week period by shoveling snow. Study the graph and answer the following questions.

1. Without figuring, can you tell which boy made more money? Check your estimate.
2. In which week was a record set for earning the most money? Who set it? How much money did he make? How much more did he make that week than the other boy?
3. What happened in the week ending January 29?
4. Something is implied by the information given for the week ending January 22. What must have happened during that week?
5. What other information is given in this graph?

THE STRAY CUR

Hunger

The dog had no name. For a dog to have a name someone must have him and someone must love him, and a dog must have someone. The dog had no one, and no one had the dog. The dog had only the silent empty countryside of the few houses. The dog had only the crumbs and cleaned bones he could pick up at the few houses. The dog had only himself, so the dog had nothing, and he was afraid.

He was a scared little whip-tailed cur. He was a stray, and he seemed to have been born a stray. He clung to a small area of countryside just a few miles outside a town. In a furtive, hidden, almost wild-animal way he had made it his own. Here the houses were few, and where houses are few, people are few, and he was afraid. He was afraid of people.

But even though the people were few, the dog kept himself to the back fields, the wood lots, the fence rows and hedgerows, the shadows. The wood lots were shadowy and dark—hiding places, lurking places where the dog could live unseen. The fence rows and hedgerows were weedy and thorny and deep—secret traveling avenues by which the dog could move about unnoticed and unseen by the people and the other dogs of the countryside.

Hunger drove the dog to the few scattered houses of the people, but only at night. At night—well after midnight—when all light and life were gone from the houses, he made his rounds. He knew every house.

He knew the houses where the watchdogs lived, and he knew the houses where there were no dogs. He knew the houses where at night the dogs were kept locked up to bark uselessly at him when he made his stealthy darkness rounds. He knew the dogs of that whole countryside, but saw to it that they knew him only as a scent and a stealthy movement roundabout their houses in the night. But much more important to the all-important knowledge of his nightly meager sources of food, the little dog knew the houses where the women shook out the tablecloths outdoors. He knew at which houses the women set out too much food for the early-roosting chickens. He scoured up the crumbs; he finished off the picked-over chicken food; he dug up the buried bones of the dogs so that he might live another night.

Hunger haunted the dog. It sat like an agony back of his eyes. Hunger ached out of his ladder-rack ribs, those lean ribs that threatened to break through the stretched, shivering skin. Always the dog shivered. When at rest, he shivered. Not from cold necessarily, but from hunger, from fear, from loneliness, and from lovelessness—mostly, perhaps, from lovelessness, for the dog had nothing but himself.

Sometimes the haunting hunger drove the little dog out of his wood lot hiding places by day. But only when hunger became bigger than fear. Only on days when he had not been able to find a dead rabbit or crow, or hadn't been able to catch a quick, scurrying field mouse. On such days he would emerge from his shadowy wood lots. By secret avenues of hedgerow and fence row he would whip himself across the furtive fields to still another wood lot. In the hope of finding something dead there, or of catching a mouse there. In that hope.

And sometimes on those furtive trips from wood lot to wood lot he was seen. A woman looking out of a window might see a distant flash of something brown and white, but it would be little more than a streak and a shadow going into the shadows. Sometimes a man working in a field would catch a movement from the corner of his eye, but the flash and the shadow would be gone even as the man jerked his eyes around to search it out. That was all the dog was to anyone in that countryside —a flash and a shadow gone into the shadows. It wasn't a particular dog that they had seen before; it was just the shadowy movement of what they supposed to be a dog. No one in that countryside really knew the dog existed. No one was sure. Still the dog had lived there for a year.

But now in the last two weeks of his stray year the little dog had added a house on another road to his nightly rounds. A house where two old people lived with a toothless, rheumatic old hound. The hound was too toothless to gnaw his bones, too old and weary with life to bury his bones. But still the old hound obeyed his dog instincts and shoved his bones under an old burlap bag against the wall of a shed where he lay during the day sunning his rheumatic joints. And the little dog knew.

Now in the last week the dying old hound had even become too weary with life to eat the pan of mushy meat and vegetables set out for him every evening. And the little dog knew. Oh, how he knew, for because of the toothless old hound, the little dog had not gone hungry for a week. It was the first time in his year-long stray life. The house of the two old people became his first stop on his nightly rounds of the dark houses of the countryside.

The Memory of Fear

The little dog sat shivering in the wood lot. A night wind was sighing among the pines. The creek rustled in the night.

Under the deep-branched pines the little dog sat sorrowing.

It was over. The old dog was dead. The enameled food pan had been cleaned. His brief happiness, the security of regular food was over.

Miserably out of his stretched throat rose the thin, piercing whine. It sang about his head under the low-boughed pines. It went on and on, unloved and empty. He could not stop it.

The old life of hunger and loneliness and fear was back. He had nothing but himself and a memory.

The little dog's memory began in fear. In that memory he had not been born a stray, had not always been a stray, but almost immediately his fear and frightened bewilderment had begun. It began as of that cold moment when hands lifted him out of the warm nest where with his puppy brothers he was snuggled against the great warm body of his mother.

This time the hands that lifted him did not replace him in the nest as always before. Already in his dim puppy sight he was miles away from his mother and his puppy nest, the moment he was lifted. He stayed in the air, in the hands. He was carried away. Excited voices were right above him. The faint warm odor of his mother left him. Next the smell of the house in which he had been born went away. He was outdoors in cold, stinging air.

He was being carried along a street. Thunderous noises clapped against his ears from everywhere. Those noises were all around him; above him there was the constant, excited chatter of the little boy who was carrying him, and of the little girl who was walking tightly against her brother to be as close to the puppy as possible.

The little dog was bringing excited happiness to the two children. They had bought him, now they were carrying him home. Now he was their dog. The puppy, of course, understood none of this. The puppy only understood in a confused way the goneness of the warm, secure mother and the nest. The sharpness and coldness of the outside air hit him where the boy's arm did not shelter him. But somehow, little as he was, the puppy dimly sensed the love and excitement in the two voices above him. He somehow knew that he was being loved in a new way.

It was only when the boy and girl, playfully experimenting with their treasure, set him down, that the sharpness of the loss of nest and mother pierced into the puppy's heart. There he stood spraddle-legged, staring up in bewildered milky-eyed near-sightedness at the two white faces far above him. Desperately he whimpered up at the faces, as he stood shivering in the great strange world on a cold, hard slab of sidewalk. "Aw, poor little thing, he's so cold," the girl said. She scooped him up and cradled him in soft warm arms. "It's my turn now," she told her brother. "He's mine, too, you know."

Then there was another house. No mother, no brothers, no sisters were in this house. No nest. No furry warmth to snuggle into, snuggle and drink, crawl under and into, deeper and warmer, to sleep and drink warm milk. No nest in which to wrestle with another soft puppy with fierce puppy growls, only in the midst of the battle to forget and fall asleep. Another house—a cold house, cold-clean house with hard clean smells; no mother, sister, brother smells.

There were new voices. The heavier voices of a man and woman in among the excited shrill voices of the little boy and girl. He was set down on the kitchen linoleum. There he stood. His spraddled-out puppy legs slipped farther apart on the cold, slippery, waxed linoleum. He slid, legs in every direction, down into a clumsy little puppy heap.

He looked up from his helpless little heap, and all the voices above roared as one great roar. The laughter roared until the laughter shrieked. Suddenly he was terribly afraid. "Watch him!" the woman screamed. All the laughter stopped. The puppy was jerked up from the floor by the scruff of his neck. He felt himself dangling, sailing. A door opened, and he was dropped. The door banged shut. He was all alone in the cold outdoors. He had landed too hard. He sat whining softly where he had landed, understanding none of it.

The door opened, the little girl was picking him up, cuddling him in her soft warm arms. Her face nuzzled his woolly fur. "You didn't know, did you? You don't know about houses yet."

She carried him back into the kitchen. He felt a little more secure because it was warm in her arms. Suddenly the woman's big white face loomed close. The puppy looked up at her. "Not even housebroken," the woman said harshly near the puppy's ear. "Isn't this going to be something!"

"Oh, we'll take care of it, Mother," the girl promised anxiously. "We'll watch him and train him... ."

The woman made snorting noises. "Yes, yes, I know those promises—good for a day or so, and then it'll be up to me. Believe me, he's going to learn fast, I'll see to that.... But he is a cute tike," she said more calmly. Her face came closer still. The puppy shrank back against the girl.

The man's big round face was thrust beside the woman's. "Nicely marked," the man said. "But it doesn't look to me as if he's got much spirit. Some dogs start out feeling whipped, you know." His face stayed there. "Housebroken, hah!" his voice exploded. "Looks to me as if he mightn't even be weaned yet. You kids got him too soon. I suppose you couldn't wait, but it would be a mercy if you took him back to his mother for another week.... I doubt he can even drink out of a saucer."

The puppy was lowered to the floor. He was placed before a saucer of cold milk.

He sprawled before the saucer, his weak little legs started slipping. He didn't even see the white milk in the white saucer; it had no known smell, just a cold, chalky smell. The puppy didn't want it, didn't need it, didn't know it. Suddenly his nose was thrust into the cold milk. "Got to show them how at first," the man's voice said.

Cold sticky milk stuffed his nostrils. The puppy choked, splattered milk. "Now look, John, what you made him do!" the woman screeched. "Two minutes in the house and already two messes on my clean floor, and I just waxed it."

Now the boy grabbed the puppy. The boy rubbed his hand over the puppy's nose, rubbing away the cold stickiness of the milk. The puppy sneezed.

"Can't baby him too much. Start out that way and you'll soon have a dog nobody can do anything with," the father instructed. "Try him with some warm milk, he's not used to cold milk."

There was the saucer again, the milk, white and thin with a little steaminess curling up from it. But now the puppy was afraid of the white saucer. He squirmed under the hand that shoved him toward the milk. He whined when he couldn't squirm free; he bared his sharp little teeth.

"See that? See that? Wanted to bite me. He's got spirit all right," the man exclaimed. The big sure voice knew all about puppies, and what should

be done. "Well, we'll have to cure him of that. Break their spirit first, then build it up again—your way. That's the way to get a good trained dog. Of course, you can't start yet, he's too young. So we'll just teach him to drink first." The puppy's face was shoved into the milk, the hand pressed down. The puppy choked, he struggled, his nails scrabbled on the smooth linoleum. Milk got in his eyes.

"Maybe he isn't hungry," the little girl said in a tiny, wretched voice. "Please, Dad . . ."

"Puppies are always hungry," the man's sure voice said. "He's just not weaned yet. You two take him back for a week or so. Then when you get him again he won't be so helpless and we can start training him a bit."

The girl and boy began to cry.

Of course, the puppy understood none of this. He knew nothing of laughter and weeping and talk. It only added to his bewilderment and coldness. That is what he understood the best—the coldness which meant being separated from his mother. He was spraddling on the cold floor, forgotten by the weeping children who were pleading with their father. The father softened. "All right, all right! You two win, we'll keep him, feed him with a medicine dropper if we have to—just so you stop your yammering. But one thing—see to it that you help your mother take care of him."

"Hah, easy talk for you," the woman said. "I'm the one that's going to have the mess. They'll fuss the little animal half to death the first couple of days, but once the novelty is worn off . . ."

The children broke off their sobbing; they'd won. Everybody at the same time remembered the puppy.

"Now where'd he crawl to?"

He had crawled to a dark space between the stove and the wall. There was a little warmth there. The little dog sat pressed against the stove, hugging the slight feeling of warmth that seeped through the oven wall from the oven pilot light. They found him.

"Now why'd he crawl there? Look quick, I suppose he went there to make a mess again," the woman said.

A big hand reached into the narrow space. The puppy pressed back against the wall. But the hand came on. The puppy growled, bared his teeth, desperately scared of the poking hand. He growled little puppy growls, warning the hand away.

"Listen to that, will you?" the woman said, half amused, half in alarm. "He wanted to bite me! He isn't going to be a mean dog, is he?"

Later, quiet came, and the dark, and the cold—except for the feeble seeping warmth from the oven of the gas stove. The puppy was in the narrow space, the first place where he had felt a little warmth and a little safety. But now the house was quiet and strange and hostile. There were no voices now, only deep breathings from behind a closed door. The puppy scrabbled at the old sweater the little girl had shoved into the space between the wall and the stove. He rumpled it; he tried to snuggle into it; he crawled under a sleeve but his little head emerged from the other side of the sleeve. Then the loose sweater slipped away from him entirely over the waxy floor, it was gone. The puppy raised his head and whined out his misery and loneliness. When he had started he could not stop the whine; it shrieked higher and higher, and in it were all his loneliness, coldness, and fear.

There were stumbling noises. The man's hard voice clapped into the little space beside the stove. "Quiet. Quiet, you . . ."

It flattened the puppy, scared the whining out of him until there was only the thin tickle of a whimper left down in his throat. "I know you're homesick, but I've got to sleep, I've got to go to work in the morning." The reasonableness left the voice in the irritation of disrupted sleep. "You're going to yammer wherever you are, so down to the cellar you go. I've got to get some sleep."

The man jerked the puppy out of the corner. Barefooted and sleepy the man went down the cellar steps, pulled a paper carton from somewhere, fumbled around, found some newspapers and rags, dropped them to the bottom of the carton, dropped the puppy on top of them. The light went out, the cellar door was shoved shut, darkness settled in the cellar, darkness in the box. The first whimper came squeezing out of the puppy's throat. It rose. It bounced back at him from the four sides of the box and echoed away in the deep cellar. The echo fooled him, made him stop to listen. It was almost as if he'd heard a brother puppy whimper back. And then it rose up out of him, higher, higher, without letup, tearing his little throat. He couldn't stop it. Only his mother, his home, his nest could stop it.

Soft careful noises came down the cellar steps. Bare feet were carefully feeling their way down the dark steps. There were cautious whispers. There were the little girl and boy, fearful in the dark gloom of the cellar, fearful of being heard by the parents. And then the puppy was cuddled in a warm lap; warm, soft hands stroked him. There they sat, shivering, whispering, loving.

The cellar door ripped open. Light flooded the basement. "John, they're here. Down in the cellar with that dog!"

The man came, sleepy, yawning. "How long have you two been down there?"

"Oh, we just came, Daddy . . . ."

"What a night, what a night," the man was grumbling. "Well, back to bed with you, and don't you ever dare to do that again."

"But, Dad, he cried so."

"Well, you can't sit up with him nights. Back to your beds right now."

"But he'll cry so." The boy, George, was almost crying himself.

"All right," his mother said at last. "I'll put a hot-water bottle in with him, and wrap it in that old fur piece of mine. If I do that, will you promise to go right back to sleep?"

"Oh, yes, Mama."

They all disappeared. Later the woman came back alone and started fussing in the deep carton box. She was yawning and shivering. "You must be dead tired yourself. Go to sleep now."

Soothed into it by the warmth rising up from the hot-water bottle under the fur piece; fooled by the fur—dead fur, but live, lovely warmth—he slept.

 **Furtive** means "done stealthily" or "secret." It comes from the Latin word for thief, *fur*. Although furtive no longer means "thief," it has retained much of the original flavor of its root. And a thief would certainly be furtive in his actions!

What Do You See?

Perhaps you have had an experience similar to this. For months your brother talked about his friend Jerry. From hearing about him—how he looked, what he was like—and from speaking with him over the phone, you had a clear image of Jerry. Then one day you met him . . . His hair and eyes were the color your brother had said they were. But he wasn't the Jerry you had pictured.

In reading, something very similar happens. No matter how carefully a writer chooses his words, no two readers will have the same mental images when they read his story.

Try the following experiment. Think about the story "The Stray Cur," page 221. Write a description of the dog. How big was he? What color was he? If he had spots, where were the spots?

Think about the countryside and the woodlot and write descriptions of them.

After you have finished writing your descriptions, take turns reading them aloud. Note how differently each "saw" the things he had read about in the story.

Now turn to "April Rain Song," page 218. Reread this poem and write a description of the things your mind's eye sees when you think of April rain.

As you read, always try to form images of what the author is describing.

HIGHWAYS OF THE SEAS

At this very moment there are thousands of bottles bobbing about on oceans. Most are discards but some have messages inside that tell us many things about the seas and about the people who sail them.

One day in 1947 two boys were exploring the beach along the New England coast. A storm had just passed, and the shore was littered with wreckage. Among the rubble the boys found a bottle with this message inside:

Our Ship is sinking. The S.O.S. won't help. I guess this is it. Good-bye now---- Maybe this will reach the good old U.S.A.

After the boys had handed the message over to the authorities, it was learned that the bottle and the wreckage had come from the U. S. destroyer *Beatty*. On November 6, 1943, during World War II, the *Beatty* had been sunk by an enemy torpedo as she was entering the Mediterranean Sea. This message, tossed into the sea by an unknown sailor, had bobbed across the Atlantic Ocean for thousands of miles until it was washed ashore four years later.

It's exciting to think about a lone bottle bobbing across the rolling seas with a message from someone who was on a sinking ship or stranded on a desert island. However, less exciting, but of greater value, are the bottles set adrift by scientists. And although scientists have many instruments for studying ocean currents, they frequently float bottles on the seas. From their studies we now know that these currents are like huge rivers flowing through the seas. They are started and kept moving mainly by wind currents and the earth's rotation. The temperature, the depth of the ocean, and irregularities of the coastline also cause the waters to move.

Scientists have discovered just how man's life is affected by ocean currents. For instance, we know that ocean currents help make climate. In the northern hemisphere one of the major currents is the Gulf Stream, which begins in the Gulf of

Mexico—just off the southern tip of Florida—and flows northeastward across the Atlantic Ocean.

Winds off the Gulf Stream warm the British Isles. The Isles are quite damp and receive abundant rainfall due to the effect of the Gulf Stream. As the warm winds blow off the ocean and onto the land, they are cooled. In cooling, these winds are forced to give up their moisture. The famous London fog is partly a result of the warm moist air blowing off the Gulf Stream and meeting the cooler air over the land. Although parts of North America and Europe have the same latitude as the British Isles, the climate is much colder.

After World War II, ships were in danger of being blown up by stray mines which had wandered into the ocean currents and were being carried by them. To chart these currents, Navy scientists released hundreds of bottles, traced their paths, determined the directions the drifting mines would be most likely to take, and then mapped out danger areas for ships to avoid. In tracing these ocean currents, scientists discovered that the currents can speed ships and rafts to their destinations. You can understand, then, why ocean currents are the "Highways of the Seas."

The study of ocean currents has interested men for hundreds of years. Why was it, people wondered, that some sailing ships and rafts reached a given

port long before others? Why was the climate of some northern countries fairly mild, whereas that of others was bitterly cold?

As far as we know, Theophrastus, a Greek scientist and philosopher who lived about 250 B.C., was the first person to make a study of ocean currents. He released bottles in the Mediterranean Sea and studied their courses.

About two thousand years later, Benjamin Franklin became interested in ocean currents. Then on a trip to England, he found that certain sailing ships from America reached England sooner than others. A whaling captain told Franklin that he had followed a great "river" that flowed out of the Gulf of Mexico. A ship traveling in that river could cross the Atlantic faster than one traveling another route.

Franklin returned home, located the river, and threw bottles into it. Sealed inside the bottles were slips of paper with Franklin's name, address, and a request that the finder contact him and tell where the bottle was found. On receiving this information, Franklin was able to chart the speed and direction of what is now known as the Gulf Stream.

There are several major currents in the world's oceans. The paths of these currents vary somewhat from year to year. A current may change course slightly or move at a different rate of speed for many reasons.

Scientists record the changes of currents because such changes affect the plant and animal life of the sea, the people who depend on the sea for a living, and those whose lives might be altered by changes in weather or climate. A change in current

Gulf Stream

may alter the food supply for the fish of a given area. And a shift in current frequently causes a change in water temperature, which can affect the hatching of fish. Also, a region's rainfall could be altered by a change in a current's course. If changes in currents are charted and people can be told what to expect, many hardships can be avoided.

To help keep track of these shifts in the currents, and for other scientific studies as well, a department of the U.S. Navy sends out several thousand bottles a year to ship captains who drop them into the oceans all over the world. Each bottle contains two cards. On the first card the captain writes the name of his ship, the date, and the exact location where the bottle is dropped into the sea. On the second card are instructions to the finder printed in seven different languages. Most of the bottles are weighted with sand to make them float upright. Then they are corked and sealed with wax to make them watertight.

Bottle voyagers usually travel about ten miles a day, twisting and turning on the huge waves. Sometimes, however, bottles caught in storms or swift currents have gone as far as eighty miles a day.

Not all bottles travel great distances and not all find their ways into currents. Instead, many travel only a few miles and then are carried to shore with the tide.

Of course many bottle voyagers are never found, but a surprisingly large number are recovered and reveal amazing stories about the ocean and the people who have lived, worked, and died there. So if you find one of these voyagers from the Highways of the Seas, look inside. There may be a fascinating story just waiting to be told!

---

1. Why do the British Isles remain warmer than parts of Canada in the same latitude?
2. Why is it important that scientists study ocean currents?
3. Was Benjamin Franklin's study of the Gulf Stream helpful to scientists? Why or why not?
4. If you were sailing across the Atlantic, how could information about the ocean currents help you?

The Greek word *klima* meant "slope" or "zone." This was derived in Latin to *climat*, "what refers to a zone." *Climat* was borrowed into English as **climate,** the overall weather conditions in a certain zone.

MAJOR JOHN WESLEY POWELL

As the four heavily laden boats glided down the quiet river, ten men stared at the surrounding countryside. On both sides rose high walls, red in the setting sun. Then the walls widened and formed a little valley. A small stream wound its way through the valley to the river. Along its banks kingfishers played. Kingfisher Canyon the men called it. For awhile they pulled their oars in and floated quietly.

"Well, Major, the Green River hardly seems dangerous around here," Jack Sumner spoke to their leader. "When do you think we will have a little excitement?"

"Always remember, Jack, that all rivers can be treacherous—especially unexplored rivers." The major studied the man next to him.

Jack Sumner was an adventurer who was tired of being a mountain guide. He was looking for new thrills, and this expedition had seemed like a good way to find them. Most of the Green and Colorado rivers had never been explored.

"It will be dark soon," the major went on. "We'll camp in the valley tonight. I'd like to do some exploring."

"Think you'll find any fossils around here?" Sumner laughed.

"Perhaps." The major waved the other three boats to shore.

While the men set up camp, the major wandered through the valley. As a scientist he was interested in discovering the secrets of this unknown part of the country. He hoped to learn how the mountains and valleys had been formed, and he wanted to map the area. He also hoped to discover some fossils. They should indicate the age of the rocks and the creatures that once lived here.

The major searched the ground and idly picked up a stick. "1869" he scratched in the dirt with his one hand. He had lost an arm in the war seven years before.

"Plunder! Come and get it!" The shout rang through the valley. The major hurried back to the campsite. The fresh air had made him hungry for a big meal.

Next morning the boats took to the water again. Now the canyon walls were close to half a mile high. They went up in steps; a clean cliff, a wooded slope, and a clean cliff again. Red Canyon they called it. The color was so bright it made the explorers' eyes smart.

Suddenly the major, Wes Powell, heard a low drumming sound. "Rapids ahead!" he called. "Looks like you'll get some excitement now, Jack."

"Are we going to run them, Major?" Sumner asked.

"We'll try it, they shouldn't be too rough here."

In a few seconds the drumming increased to a deep roar. It sounded like a thunderstorm ahead of

them. The thunderous sound of the water echoed from the canyon walls. The men in the boats began to panic.

The river swept around a bend. The water dashed and swirled about huge boulders. The men grabbed the sides of their boats and hung on as their boats were flung like matchsticks through the white water.

The men shouted, but the sound of their voices was lost in the roar of the river. Soon the boats were full of water, but the watertight compartments kept them afloat and their supplies dry.

When the men realized that they weren't sinking, they began to enjoy the thrill of the ride. They

whooped and shouted as they sped along. Suddenly they were in calm water again.

"Best ride I've had in years," Sumner grinned at the major. "Hope we run a lot of rapids."

"We'll find plenty of rapids, but if they're any worse we won't run them," Powell replied. "I have to bring ten men alive through fifteen hundred miles of canyon. We're not taking any chances just for thrills."

"But unloading four boats and portaging around the rapids is hard work," Jack grumbled.

"Maybe, but carrying them is a lot safer," Powell reminded him.

The ride through Red Canyon was pleasant. It brought them to a natural campsite called Brown's Hole. Here the party stayed for several days to study the countryside.

In the evenings Major Powell had time to gaze at the stars and think. He was finally realizing his great ambition. He was reading George Crookham's "Great Book of the Earth."

As a boy in Jackson, Ohio, he had gone for a time to a private school run by George Crookham. The school had two rooms. One was a museum where Crookham kept his fossils, rocks, plants, shells, and stuffed animals; the other was the classroom. Crookham also had a large library. He often read these books to the children. But what he enjoyed most was the study of the "Great Book of the Earth."

One day George Crookham told the class they would study the "Great Book." He took them across the fields and through the woods to a swiftly moving stream. Crookham seated himself on the bank, and the boys joined him there.

"But where is the 'Great Book'?" Wes asked.

"Why, look around you!" Crookham spread out his arms. "It is the trees and the hills, the rivers and the soil. It is the story of the earth. If we but know how to read it, we can learn everything that has happened through billions of years."

Wes looked downstream where the water cut through low cliffs. The cliffs were made up of rocks of many colors. "Can you read the story of those cliffs, Mr. Crookham?" Wes asked.

The teacher stood up and walked along the stream bed to the cliffs. He studied the layers of various colored rocks for a minute. Then with a grunt he took a knife and chipped something out. He brought it back and showed it to Wes.

"Know what this is?" the teacher asked.

"Looks like a shell, sir," Wes replied.

"Have you ever seen such a shell before?"

"No, sir," Wes shook his head.

"That's because this is a sea shell," the teacher explained. "The kind that would come from an animal which lived in salt water. We know, then, that the ocean once covered this land. When the ocean disappeared, mud and sand from the ocean floor hardened around the shells of the dead animals. We can tell how old rocks are by the geological age of the creatures found in them. Do you see now how we can read the Great Book of the Earth?"

"Yes, sir." Wes was getting excited. "If I dig in the ground near my home, could I find such shells?"

"Perhaps, but why dig when the river has done it for you?" Crookham asked. "Always follow the rivers. The walls around them are the pages of the Great Book of the Earth."

Wes never forgot George Crookham's words. Here along the Green and Colorado rivers were many pages of the Great Book. And he, Wes Powell, would be the first man ever to read them. What an awesome thought!

The men continued their trip down the river. In the first few weeks they had lost one boat in dangerous rapids. Luckily, the men had been saved. Now they all listened willingly to the major when he told them to portage.

One of the best boatmen proved to be George Bradley. He was interested in exploring, and he usually accompanied the major on his side trips.

One day the men found themselves deep in a winding canyon. On the high cliffs they could see pine forests, but by the river there was only baking rock. Powell wanted to explore the surrounding territory. Toward evening he signaled the boats to shore.

Powell and Bradley began to climb the steep cliff. There were many ledges along the way. Bradley went first, and the major, despite his missing arm, followed closely behind.

In one place Powell jumped from one foothold to the next. Too late he realized his mistake. The next ledge was too far away. He couldn't safely jump backward either.

"George," he called, "I'm rimmed!"

Bradley, on a ledge above, looked down. He could see Powell but he couldn't reach him. They hadn't brought along any rope. There was no brush near the ledge. If Powell lost his grip, he would plunge to the river far below.

There was just one thing Bradley could do. Quickly he jerked off his trousers. Bracing his legs, he lowered the pants to Powell.

The major felt his legs trembling. Then his arm began to tremble. He couldn't hold on much longer. He would have to lean backward from the cliff and make a grab for the trousers. If he missed, there would be no second chance.

He made it! Slowly Bradley hauled him up.

"If your pants were any shorter I wouldn't be alive now," Powell grinned weakly at Bradley.

They continued their climb. Suddenly the major whooped with joy. He bent down and dug something out of a rock.

"Hang on to this, George, while we go back down." Powell handed the object to Bradley.

As they approached the camp, they heard the now familiar cry, "Plunder!"

After the meal the men stretched out around the campfire. Powell asked Bradley for the object he had found in the rocks.

"Know what this is?" Powell asked the men. Silence greeted him. "Fossil—shark's tooth—millions of years old."

"What's it doing around here?" Jack Sumner questioned as he came over for a closer look.

"According to these rocks, this area has been covered by the ocean three times. The red rock in the cliffs is sandstone, formed during the times when the land was covered by water. The white rock is limestone, made up of millions of tiny sea animals that lived in the oceans."

"You mean we're really exploring the bed of a great ocean?" Bradley asked.

"Yes," Powell replied. "If you men could realize that, you'd get much more out of this trip. You'd find the earth's history as exciting as running rapids."

The major knew that most of the men were not convinced. They were adventurers, not scientists. But it didn't matter. He needed adventurers, too. Without them he could never have made this trip. Ahead of them lay the Colorado River just waiting to unlock its secrets. Soon this section of the map would no longer be marked "unexplored."

"Follow the rivers," George Crookham had said. And as Wes Powell did just that, the pages of the Great Book of the Earth opened all around him.

---

1. What was the "Great Book of the Earth" mentioned in this story? Do you enjoy studying that "book"? What part of it do you enjoy studying the most?

2. Was Major Powell a good leader for an expedition? Why or why not?

3. Would you have wanted to travel with Powell? Why or why not?

The suffix *-logy* meaning "any science or branch of knowledge," is from the Greek *logos*, "speech, or account." *Ge* is Greek for "earth." **Geology** is what is said and thought about the earth. *Psyche* means "mind, spirit"; what is *psychology*?

THE CANOE IN THE RAPIDS

The time: long ago. The place: Canada. The winter
wind howls about the house and snow piles deeper and
deeper outside. But inside it is cozy and warm, and best
of all, there is a visitor, Michel Meloche—Uncle Michel
to everyone in the north woods. He is a woodsman who
spends most of his time trapping or working in lumber
camps. Occasionally he stops at the home of a friend or
relative for a night or two.

Yes, everyone is quiet as Uncle Michel walks to the
woodbox to clean his pipe, for they know that a story is
about to begin. Uncle Michel will turn this humble
kitchen into an enchanted theater.

Once in another time, François Ecrette was an adventurer in the woods. Every winter he went north with Sylvain Gagnon. They trapped foxes, beavers, minks, and any furred creature that would step into their traps.

When spring came and the ice in the river melted, the two men would load their furs into a canoe and paddle down the swift current to sell their winter's catch to the trader.

It was one such spring that François and Sylvain headed south with the finest catch that they had ever made. If only they could beat the other trappers to the trading post, they could make a fine bargain.

"A-ah, we will be rich men," said Sylvain, who already could hear the tintin of coins in his deep pockets.

"Yes," answered François, "if we get through the Devil's Jaws safely."

Nowhere on any of the rivers of Canada was there such a fearsome place. In the Devil's Jaws, there were waterfalls that roared and whirlpools that spun a boat about like a dry leaf. It was as if the river fell into a panic itself when squeezed into the Devil's Jaws and tried to run away in every direction.

"That's true," said Sylvain, "but you are lucky to have me for a partner. Nowhere in all Canada is there such a skillful boatman as Sylvain Gagnon."

Sylvain drew the cold air in through his nose and puffed out his chest with it.

So François Ecrette felt safe and happy, even though the worst ordeal of the long trip was ahead of them.

They loaded the canoe with their bundles of furs and their provisions. For days they paddled down the river, singing gay songs to pass away the long hours.

259

One late afternoon they beached their boat on the bank and made for a clearing on the hill. They built a campfire, and François started to roast a young rabbit he had shot. He hung it over the coals by spearing it on a green willow branch.

"We must eat well," said Sylvain, "for we are close to the Devil's Jaws. We will need all our strength for that pull and push."

"But it will soon be dark," François reminded him. "Shouldn't we camp here all night so we can go through the rapids in daylight?"

"Pou, pou," laughed Sylvain, "what a scared rabbit you are! I can paddle at night as well as by day. I could shoot the Devil's Jaws with my eyes closed and a beaver riding on my paddle."

François rubbed his stubbly chin.

"My faith," he exclaimed, "I am the luckiest man in the world to have you for a partner, Sylvain Gagnon. I don't believe you have fear of anything."

As if to test the truth of this, an angry growl came from behind the bushes. Both men jumped to their feet, François seizing his rifle as he did so. The bushes broke open and a big brown bear came through them. He walked slowly on all fours, shuffling from this paw to that paw, and from that paw to this paw. Straight toward the two trappers he came.

François lifted his rifle to his shoulder and took careful aim. He pulled the trigger. Plink! Nothing happened. There was no bullet in the rifle because it had been used on the rabbit.

The bear gave another angry growl. He rose on his hind legs and walked toward François like a man, shuffling from this paw to that paw.

François dropped the gun and ran for his life. Already Sylvain Gagnon was far ahead of him, his fur coat making him look like a bear that ran too fast to shuffle from this paw to that paw. François made for a big tree, but he didn't have time to climb it as the bear was almost on him. So around the tree he ran. And behind him followed the bear. Round and round and round the tree ran François and the bear. Any little bird looking down from the treetop wouldn't have known whether the bear was chasing François Ecrette or François was chasing the bear. The trapper ran so fast that he was more behind the bear than in front of him. And as the bear ran around the tree, he clawed the air angrily. But his sharp claws only tore the bark from the tree. And if François had anything at all to be thankful for, it was that the ragged shreds flying through the air were bark from the tree and not skin from his back.

Around and around and around went the man and the beast. The bear got dizzy first. He ran slower and slower. Finally he broke away from the tree and went staggering away, first to this side and then to that side. And as he reeled and stumbled, he knocked his head into one tree trunk after another. Bump—bump—bump.

François lost no time in finding another tree to climb, for the tree they had been running around had been stripped of its bark as far up as a bear could reach. As he climbed, he could hear the bump, bump, bump of the bear's head as he stumbled into tree trunks.

Panting and dizzy himself, François settled into a crotch of the tree. Now where was that false friend, Sylvain Gagnon, who had left him to face the bear alone? He called and called but there was no answer. Perhaps the bear had eaten Sylvain. A-tout-tou, what bad luck that would be when there was still the Devil's Jaws ahead! How could he ever get through those treacherous waters without the skillful boatman Sylvain Gagnon?

And how could he get safely from the tree to the boat? Perhaps the bear was waiting for him among the bushes. The sleepy sun soon went to

bed and it grew dark. It became colder than ever. François Ecrette's arms and legs were numb.

At last he jerkily lowered himself from the tree. He looked about in every direction, but it was too dark to see anything. He sniffed and sniffed like a bear, for if a bear can smell a man, maybe a man can smell a bear. But all François could smell was the sharp, icy air of early spring. Slowly he made his way down the hill toward the place they had left the canoe.

Then great joy filled the heart of François Ecrette. Although the trees blackened the river, a faint moonlight glimmered through them. Its pale light fell upon a figure hunched in the bow of the canoe with the fur coat pulled up over its ears.

"Sylvain," cried François, "you are safe after all. Why didn't you come back to me?"

But Sylvain must have felt a deep shame, for he only put his head down between his arms and made a sad, apologetic sound.

"Believe me, my friend," said François, "I'm certainly glad you escaped, for we have a terrible ride ahead of us this night. Do you think we better try the rapids after all?"

But his companion resolutely straightened up and squared his shoulders in the fur coat. François pushed the boat into the stream, leaped aboard and grabbed a paddle. Silently they floated into the current; then the slender canoe headed for the dangers ahead.

"My faith, it is good to have you in this boat with me," cried François. "This current is like a bolt of lightning."

The boat raced faster and faster. Instead of paddling for speed, François had to spend his strength flattening the paddle like a brake. The trees made a dark tunnel of the river course so that François could barely see his companion's stout back.

On, on they went. The frail canoe sped in a zigzag flight like a swallow. François Ecrette's sharp ear caught the distant roar of the rapids.

"Brace yourself, Sylvain," he cried, "for the boat is now in your hands. I will help you as much as I can."

So he plied his paddle from this side to that side and from that side to this side. The river had become like an angry, writhing eel. He heard the waterfall ahead and began paddling like mad so the canoe would shoot straight and true. The least slant of the boat and the churning current would turn it over and over, and swallow them both.

François felt the icy wind and the cold spray on his face as they plunged over the waterfall and bobbed in the whirlpool below. He fought the churning, frothing waters that he could hear more than see. His muscles tightened like iron and the air blew up his lungs.

"My faith, but it's a good thing to have such a boatman as Sylvain Gagnon guiding this canoe," rejoiced François. "In such a current as this, no other man could bring a boat through safely. I will forget the way he deserted me when that big brown bear attacked us."

All danger was not over yet, for the stern of the canoe was sucked into the outer rim of a whirlpool. The lurch of the boat wrenched François Ecrette's back like a blow from a giant hammer. The canoe spun around completely. For fully ten minutes, there was such a battle with the churning waters as François had never known before. Around and around, up and down rocked the canoe, with François fiercely wielding his paddle. If it hadn't been for the soothing figure in front of him, he would have given up in fright.

Finally the canoe straightened out and leaped straight ahead. The roar of the rapids grew fainter. François let his paddle drag and relaxed.

"My faith," he gasped. "I thought that was the last of us for sure. You have saved us both, Sylvain Gagnon. No boatman in all Canada but you could have gotten us out of that Devil's trap."

But his modest companion only shrugged his shoulders and humped lower into the bow.

Then because François was worn out from his paddling, he decided to take a little nap. With no other partner but Sylvain would he have dared doze off. But Sylvain had proved his mettle in getting them through the rapids, and the waters ahead were slow and peaceful. So François rested his paddle, closed his eyes and fell into a deep sleep.

When he awoke, it was morning. The sun had chased the shadows out from under the trees, and the river sparkled in the friendliest kind of way.

François rubbed the sleep out of his eyes.

"Ah, Sylvain," he yawned, "what a night we had in the rapids. If it hadn't been for you—a-tou-tou-tou-tou!"

For François Ecrette's partner in the canoe was not Sylvain Gagnon, the great boatman, but the big brown bear of the clearing!

François jumped up and gave a bloodcurdling shriek. The bear slowly turned around and looked at him. He shook his great furry head as if to shake his brains back into their right place after they had been knocked apart by the tree trunks. He gave a low threatening growl.

François didn't wait any longer. He dived into the river and furiously swam through the icy water. After what seemed a sinner's lifetime, he

reached the frosty shore. When he looked back at the river, he had a last glance of the canoe, full of furs, disappearing among the trees with the big brown bear standing in the bow.

Now this was a fine how-does-it-make of trouble. Here was François all alone in the wilderness without Sylvain, furs, provisions or even a dry match.

Luckily the trading post couldn't be too far away now. François gathered dry wood and started a fire in the Indian way, by rubbing two sticks together. Then he stood as close to the fire as he could, to dry out his clothes. He scorched and steamed like the uneaten rabbit back on the sharp stick in the clearing.

At last he was dry enough to brave the cold walk down the river bank. He set out slowly. The branches scratched his hands and face. His boots sloshed and squashed through the slush of early spring.

It was late afternoon by the time he reached the trader's village. Everyone seemed surprised to see him alive.

"Your canoe was found caught in a log jam below here, with bear tracks on the shore," said the trader. "We thought a bear had carried you off."

"But the furs," cried François. "What happened to them? Were they lost?"

"They are all safe," said the trader. "Your friend Sylvain Gagnon arrived only a little while ago. He helped me check through them."

Then a familiar face appeared in the crowd.

"François, my good friend," cried Sylvain. "I got a ride back with a party of Indians. But how did you ever get the canoe through the rapids all by yourself?"

"Sylvain, my false friend," retorted the trapper, "I was not alone. The big brown bear who chased me in the clearing was with me."

Then François Ecrette shivered and shook in a way that had nothing to do with the cold spring afternoon or his damp clothing.

So all turned out well for François Ecrette in the end. But he never went on any more trapping trips with Sylvain Gagnon. You see, my friends, one who turns into a big brown bear when you need him most is not a true friend.

In medieval times, a person accused of a crime was put to a test. If he could escape unharmed, he was declared innocent. An Old English word for "judgment" was *ordal*. Today **ordeal** means "a trying experience."

MRS. THWICKLE'S SPECIAL CATS

Luckily for Mrs. Thwickle, who dearly loved cats, she lived in New York City where there were so many strays. Each evening she would come to the deserted house near her home to feed the cats that lived in the basement.

There was Leonore, the mother cat, and her girl kittens, Matilda, Rita, and Nesselrode. And there were two boy kittens, Theodore and Wolfgang.

Matilda was white with a black spot on the end of her tail.

Rita was black except for a white spot on the end of her tail.

Nesselrode had a black back, white belly, three white paws, and one black one.

Theodore had a white back, black belly, three black paws, and one white one.

And Wolfgang was mostly white except for a black patch over his left eye and black hind paws.

Mrs. Thwickle had always thought her stray friends were special.

She was right! And they proved that she was when something happened that forced them to take matters into their own paws.

One night when Mrs. Thwickle turned the corner of the street where the old house stood, there was no one to greet her. She hurried to the house to find out what the trouble was.

The trouble was that it was gone. There was nothing but a great big hole where the house had stood.

Mrs. Thwickle was so upset she nearly cried. She went up and down the street, and around the corner, and around the block, and she looked into doorways and alleys and she called for Leonore and for Rita and for Theodore and for Nesselrode and for Wolfgang and for Matilda.

But they had all disappeared, all of them.

When the next morning came, Mrs. Thwickle was still looking for the cats. She walked around all over downtown New York, calling the cats by name, one after the other, but each time in a different order so that none would be offended. But no cats were to be seen and Mrs. Thwickle was very sad. She did not know what was happening at that very moment a few miles away, in midtown Manhattan.

It was the morning rush hour up there.

Along Fifth Avenue and Madison Avenue and Park Avenue and along all the other avenues and streets the cars and the cabs and the buses were nudging each other along, honking their horns and racing their motors. Thousands and thousands of people hurried to work, out of the subway stations and into the buildings, and across the streets among the cars and the buses and the cabs.

It was certainly no place for a cat.

But there was a cat, right there.

Two cats, in fact.

One was a black-and-white cat and you will not be surprised to hear that it was Leonore, because by now you surely know that Leonore was a special cat; and if you found any cat in the middle of New York during the morning rush hour, you would certainly expect it to be a special cat, so you should not be surprised to hear that it was Leonore.

And what was Leonore doing on Fifth Avenue? She was carrying Rita across the street by the scruff of the neck, the way one always sees cats carrying kittens in pictures. Rita was a rather big kitten now, and Leonore had a hard time carrying her by the neck, but she did.

Now if you are not familiar with New York, you should be told that it is quite unusual for a cat to carry a kitten across Fifth Avenue during the morning rush hour.

People stopped and looked.

Cars stopped.

Everything stopped.

And when Leonore reached the other side, she simply turned around and went back across the street.

By that time a police officer had reached the scene. This particular policeman (his name was Mullins) was a very experienced policeman, because you get to be experienced when you are a policeman on Fifth Avenue in New York. All kinds of things happen there every day because there are so many people around.

But Officer Mullins could not remember ever having seen a cat carry a kitten across the avenue, and still less could he remember a cat carrying a kitten across the avenue and back again, and then back once more (because that's what Leonore was doing this very minute).

But a good police officer must be able to handle unusual situations, and to Mullins it was clear what must be done: he must get the cats off the street.

He would have done it too, except for one thing.

There was a television camera standing on top of a car parked at the curb, and a man was busily filming the scene.

Officer Mullins went over to the man and asked him what was going on. Was this a TV program of some kind? And who gave them permission?

Oh, no, said the cameraman, he had just happened to be driving by on his way to a reception for

a foreign diplomat, and he had seen the commotion and stopped, and started filming it. He thought the TV audience would love it.

Mullins thought they would, too. But what would the audience think about a policeman picking up these two poor stray cats and carrying them away?

"They'll think it's terrible," said the cameraman, who could more or less guess the officer's thoughts. "Disturbing a poor cat who is just trying to help her kitten across the street."

"Across, I can understand," said the officer, "but back and forth and back and forth, I can't."

He decided to call his sergeant for further instructions.

He went to a telephone and called, but the sergeant wasn't in. Where was he? Where, in fact, was practically half the police force?

They were in the subway station at Times Square, and I'll tell you what they were doing there.

They were standing in the subway station, the policemen, deep underground, discussing strategy with Mr. Nooman.

Mr. Nooman was the motorman of a subway train. He had been driving a long, long train, packed with people, when suddenly he had seen something white in the tunnel. That is, it seemed white. Actually it was mostly white with a black spot on the tip of its tail, and it was named Matilda. But subway tunnels are quite dark and to Mr. Nooman the cat seemed to be all white, and besides, he did not know it was named Matilda.

Matilda was walking along the tracks. Mr. Nooman stopped the train because he was a nice man and did not like the idea of hitting a cat, and he jumped out of his cab and tried to catch Matilda. But every time he came near, the kitten raised a paw toward the third rail on the side which carries the electricity for the train. Now if Mr. Nooman had touched the cat while the cat was touching the rail, two things would have happened. There would have been a dead cat, and there would have been a dead Mr. Nooman. Mr. Nooman decided against it. Instead he clapped his hands in the hope that this would frighten the cat away. But Matilda just kept walking along, slowly, stopping once in a while to see if anybody was near, and raising her paw if necessary.

In the meantime, subway trains had to stop, one behind the other, and in each train thousands of people were muttering and complaining and wondering what was the matter.

If you had been way up in the air over New York at that time, in a balloon perhaps, you would have seen some very unusual things.

You would have seen the traffic jam on Fifth Avenue spread up and down the avenue and into the cross streets and up and down the next avenue, and then some more.

And farther west you would have seen people pouring out of subway stations and trying to find buses or cabs. But, of course, the buses and cabs weren't running because of the traffic jam.

And then you would have seen, still farther west where docks line the Hudson River, police cars racing to the Lincoln Tunnel, which connects New York with New Jersey under the river and is full of cars and trucks day and night.

For in the Lincoln Tunnel, a cat—to be precise, a cat with a black back and white belly and three white paws and one black paw, by the name of Nesselrode—had dashed across the roadway just in front of a big black car that was driving to New York. The car stopped. The car behind it stopped too, but not quite soon enough. It bumped into the first car. The car behind bumped into the second. And another one bumped into the third. When the first police car got there, bang-bang-bangs could still be heard from the New Jersey side; and it is quite possible that this would have gone on clear into Ohio if some driver a few miles away hadn't been careful enough to keep his distance from the car ahead, as one always should, and so could stop in time.

In the meantime, Nesselrode had quietly left the Lincoln Tunnel and was on her way to the Holland Tunnel, which is another tunnel under the river and is just as busy as the Lincoln Tunnel. Bang! Bang-bang-bang!

You and I know that there were still two cats to be heard from. Leonore and Rita were busy tying up Fifth Avenue, Nesselrode was taking care of the tunnels, and Matilda had put a few subway lines out of commission.

But where was Theodore and where was Wolfgang?

They were, you may be sure, not idle.

Theodore was down in the financial district, not far from where the old house had stood. There is a street down there named Wall Street, a rather narrow street with very, very tall buildings on both sides, and frightfully busy.

The Stock Exchange stands there, on Wall Street, and people buy and sell stocks and bonds and shares, and yell at each other, and watch quotations, and read the reports on long thin ticker tapes that come out of machines, and all over the world businessmen wait for the results of the day's tradings on Wall Street. What goes on there is very important for everybody, but why it is would take a whole long book to explain and then we would have no room left to find out about our cats.

Theodore, who was black and white and had three black paws and one white paw, was having even more fun than his sisters farther uptown. Can there be more fun than getting tangled up in ticker tape, tearing it off, racing around entangled in long streamers of it? Dashing in and out among shouting people? Frightening telephone operators half out of their wits and in general causing more confusion than the Stock Exchange had ever seen before?

It isn't often that business at the Stock Exchange is interrupted by outsiders, especially by a cat with three black paws and one white paw, and the news was all over town in minutes—in fact, all over the world, because there are direct telephone connections between Wall Street and many, many offices in different countries. And so everybody soon knew that a cat was tying up the Stock Exchange, and then people said they had heard about other cats up on Fifth Avenue, and in the subway, and in the tunnels, and before long the police came, and the reporters, and finally the foreman of the wrecking crew a few blocks away heard about the trouble, and he went up to a reporter and told him about Mrs. Thwickle and how she had said that these were very special cats and wouldn't stand for the old house being torn down.

The reporter thought it sounded interesting, so he telephoned his newspaper and was told to go out and find Mrs. Thwickle immediately, which he did.

In the meantime, Theodore had left the Stock Exchange and was trotting up Broadway toward City Hall, tail high in the air. Nobody touched him. People just stood and watched, and everybody came to the windows of the tall building, and then someone started throwing bits of paper into the street, which is what people working in offices there always do when something goes on down below on Broadway; and before you knew it you had a regular ticker-tape parade of the kind that New York always gives to generals and fliers and kings but never before to cats.

The mayor was sitting in his office in City Hall when he heard the commotion. He went to the window and saw a cat marching up Broadway with showers of ticker tape and torn-up telephone books fluttering down on him. The mayor went back to his desk and sat down and thought it over for a few moments, and then he went back to the window, but it was still a cat that he saw. At that moment the police commissioner came in.

He told the mayor about Rita and Leonore on Fifth Avenue.

He told him about Nesselrode in the Holland Tunnel.

He told him about Matilda in the subway.

He told him about Theodore in the Stock Exchange.

And then he told him something that even you do not know yet. He told him about Wolfgang in the United Nations.

A few blocks east from the streets that were now a wild tangle of honking cars stands the headquarters of the United Nations.

The General Assembly of the United Nations was holding a meeting there, and the delegates from more than ninety countries listened to speeches and argued and voted, unaware of all the excitement that was going on in other parts of New York. They were sitting in the huge hall where a small delegate from a big country was making an important speech.

In glass-enclosed rooms around the rim of the hall, reporters were busy making notes. Movie and TV cameras were on the job. Behind other glass partitions the translators were busy. They had a very hard job, for the speaker spoke rapidly, and they had to keep up with him and quickly translate everything he said into other languages. The delegates wore earphones, and they could listen to the speech in English or French or Spanish or Russian or Chinese.

The small delegate from the big country was about to make a very important point.

"And now listen carefully..." he was saying, raising a stubby finger for emphasis. Everybody listened carefully.

"*Et maintenant, écoutez . . .*" said the French translator.

" И ТЕПЕРЬ СЛУШАЙТЕ . . ." said the Russian translator.

" 你听听 . . . " said the Chinese translator.

"*Y ahora, escuchen . . .*" said the Spanish translator.

The speaker paused dramatically. Everybody looked up expectantly.

"Meow," said Wolfgang, who had quietly appeared on the speaker's platform.

"*Miau,*" said the Spanish translator.

" МЯУКАНЬЕ ," said the Russian translator.

"*Miaou,*" said the French translator.

"喵 喵," said the Chinese translator.

"Meow," the reporters noted in their notebooks.

You will notice that Wolfgang said "Meow," and not "Eyowr" as he usually did. Very few cats ever say, "Meow." Some say, "Nya," and some say, "Eeya," and some say, "Myar." But sometimes, on very special occasions, a cat will really say, "Meow"; and this certainly was a special occasion. And it was a good thing that he said, "Meow," because we can't be sure that the translators would have been able to translate "Nya" or "Eeya" or even "Myar."

Everybody jumped to their feet and yelled—in a dozen different languages—and some wanted to

chase Wolfgang out and others asked what country he represented, and before long the for-cat and against-cat debate which was going on all over New York City had spread to the United Nations.

Some delegates had to telephone their governments back home to find out which side they were supposed to be on.

When the police commissioner had finished telling the mayor about all this, the mayor looked at him and said:

"You mean to tell me six cats can tie up the City of New York?"

The police commissioner looked at the mayor and said:

"They did. And what do you want me to do, shoot them? I like cats."

The mayor looked at the police commissioner and said:

"Who said anything about shooting? But you must get the city back to normal."

The police commissioner looked at the mayor and said:

"Just the city? I understand everybody in London and Paris and Hong Kong is listening to the radio, waiting for the next move."

The mayor looked at the police commissioner and said:

"And what is the next move?"

The police commissioner looked at the mayor and said:

"Well, we have an expert in animal psychology from Heidelberg University coming in, and we are thinking of issuing pieces of liver to every policeman . . ."

Our word *ton* appeared in Middle English as *tonne* and meant "what a large cask would hold." A large cask is still called a *tun.* A **tunnel** is the shape of a very long cask, and is borrowed from a French word for barrels and funnels.

Brownstone

Birds and butterflies
dart
   down
      canyons
between tall buildings
looking for a place to hide
as the sky above the city darkens
and the rain begins
      timid at first—unsure
then creeping onto window ledges
and foraging along the sidewalk.

They're tearing down the building across the street
and the old woman who sat cushion high
behind the flower boxes
          is gone.
Even the children who played along the broken sidewalk
          have disappeared
and their hop-scotch lines are washed away.
Only the multi-colored cat
preening in the shop window
is unconcerned
as night begins.

Key Idea in a Paragraph

The key idea in a paragraph is frequently expressed in one sentence. Sometimes it appears in the first sentence; other times a writer builds an idea one sentence at a time, ending with a summary sentence. Less often, the main idea appears in a single sentence elsewhere in the paragraph.

Turn to "Monsters of Myth and Legend" on page 122. Read the following paragraphs from the selection, locate the key sentence in each, and discuss your choice: page 126, paragraph 1; page 131, paragraph 1; page 131, paragraph 2; page 132, paragraph 2.

Frequently the key idea is "spread out" through the entire paragraph. The reader must make his own summary. Read the following paragraph and write a sentence that summarizes the key idea.

Often the word *bacteria* suggests something harmful—microörganisms which breed in dirt and filth and cause disease and infection. Of many types of bacteria this is true. But we are also surrounded by helpful bacteria. Some of these cause dead plants and animals to decay, turning their remains into soil. In fact, without the decay caused by helpful bacteria, life would soon be crowded off the earth by dead plants and animals.

Unit Five   The World At Work and Play

THE COINS OF LIN FOO

How a wise magistrate once discovered a thief is told in this dramatization of an ancient Chinese legend. It is a tale of wit and wisdom, using as a background a country village and the peasants who dwell in it.

Characters

NARRATOR, a boy, elaborately dressed, dignified

PROPERTY MAN, inconspicuous in black, casual

AN LI, the magistrate, commanding respect

LIN FOO, the boy, poorly dressed, humble

WING SOONG, the widow, poorly dressed, hard-working

TWO ATTENDANTS, for the magistrate

VILLAGERS, any number, three who speak

THIEF, who moves and acts as one of the villagers

OBSERVER, who carefully follows action of play

Properties

Table for properties

Chair for Property Man

Oriental gong and small mallet

Large basket

Small stool

Small table

Stone (piece of flagstone or other flat stone)

Two sticks, bamboo if possible

Large stone jar

Pitcher of water

Tape recorder or record player and a tape or record of oriental music (optional). Recordings of oriental music on the *koto* or *kin* are available in most record libraries.

SCENE ONE: The doorway to Wing Soong's
              cottage, and the road
SCENE TWO: The road to the village
SCENE THREE: The same

The stage is bare, except for a table and chair at Upstage Left, where the PROPERTY MAN sits. All properties to be used in the play are here and are distributed at the appropriate times. There are two doors—the left one for entrances, and the right one for exits. (The curtains are pulled only twice in the play—at the beginning and at the end. Otherwise it is not necessary, since the NARRATOR marks the division between scenes, and it is traditional for the PROPERTY MAN to change properties in full view of the audience.)

MUSIC, if used, should play when no dialogue is taking place, increasing when excitement is high and becoming quiet during important scenes. The OBSERVER stands at Upstage Right and has a gong which he strikes, in Chinese tradition, to indicate the end of a scene. The NARRATOR gives his opening speech before the curtain. Then he bows graciously and leaves. When the CURTAINS are opened for Scene One, WING SOONG has taken her place on a stool Downstage Right.

DIAGRAM OF STAGE

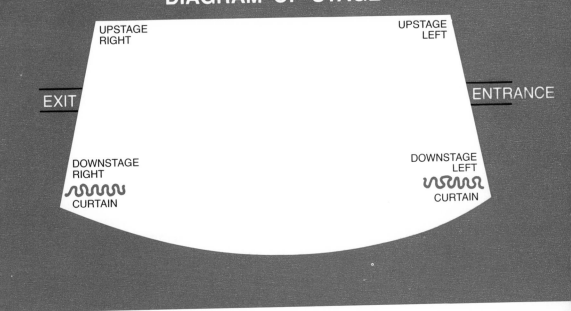

UPSTAGE RIGHT

UPSTAGE LEFT

EXIT

ENTRANCE

DOWNSTAGE RIGHT

CURTAIN

DOWNSTAGE LEFT

CURTAIN

PROLOGUE

NARRATOR. (*Walking in with great dignity to the Center of the stage where he bows three times*) Most honored ladies and gentlemen, there is an ancient legend told in China of the Magistrate and the Stone. Our players would like to perform it for you, if we may have your most gracious permission. (*Bows again, waits a moment, then goes on*) It is my humble privilege to introduce to you the characters who appear in this story. First in importance is the great magistrate, AN LI. It is said that he has never failed to solve a case brought before him, and the people all praise his wisdom and judgment. (*AN LI enters, crosses to the Center of the stage, bows courteously, then goes off on the other side. The NARRATOR continues)* In a certain small village in the state of Tain, there lives a humble widow, Wing Soong, and her only son, the little Lin Foo. Though her husband was a thrifty farmer, with rice fields of his own, drought and hard times have come, forcing the good Wing Soong to sell the land and earn a living for herself and her son. This she does by making fritters to sell on market days. Little Lin Foo takes the fritters each week in his basket, returning at night with the money from their sale. *(Announcing)* The woman, WING SOONG. *(WING SOONG enters Left and walks to the Center of the stage)* And her son, the little LIN FOO. *(LIN FOO joins WING SOONG. Both bow and exit Right)*

Others whom you will see in the play are the two ATTENDANTS of the good magistrate *(ATTENDANTS come forward together, bow, and leave briskly)*; the PROPERTY MAN, who will set the stage and hand the actors the properties they need *(PROPERTY MAN saunters forth, bows casually, and strolls off again in a bored manner)*; and all of the village folk who are called in the last scene to be witnesses at the trial. I shall not ask them to step forward now for our patient

audience will become weary of so many intro-
ductions. (*CURTAINS open*)

SCENE ONE

NARRATOR. (*Walks to a spot Downstage Right*) It
is morning. The pear trees are in blossom. Over
here we have the humble cottage of Wing Soong,
where the poor widow is just finishing her fritters
for the market.

(*The NARRATOR claps his hands, bows, goes
off. The OBSERVER strikes the gong and the
MUSIC begins to play. It plays undisturbed for
a moment while the PROPERTY MAN quietly
carries a large basket over to WING SOONG,
then returns to his chair. The MUSIC fades.*)

WING SOONG. Little Lin Foo! (*Calls again*) Little
Lin Foo!

LIN FOO. (*Crosses the stage to her*) Yes, my Mother.

WING SOONG. It is time now to take the basket of
fritters to the market place. It is said they are
having a fair in the village today; so I have made
twice as many for you to sell.

LIN FOO. Good, Mother. Then may I walk around
a bit before coming home? I should like to see
the wares on the tables, the flags of our country,
and the little carved wooden dragons and birds.

WING SOONG. Of course, my Son. Just mind you keep the money safe, and do not stay so long in the village that it grows dark on your journey home.

LIN FOO. I shall take care of the money, Mother. And you will see me coming through the gate before the first flowers have closed their petals for the night.

WING SOONG. Then be off, little Son. For the way is long, and already the village will be crowded with the farmers and their carts.

LIN FOO. Good-by, Mother. (*Starts out, makes a complete circle around the stage to indicate traveling a great distance, then leaves Right*)

WING SOONG. (*With a sigh*) How I wish that I might someday earn enough money to educate the little Lin Foo, that he might grow up to be a scholar instead of a peasant lad, selling his wares at the market. (*Wipes her eyes, then goes off Downstage Right*)

(*The PROPERTY MAN gets the stool she has been sitting on, takes it to his table, and the GONG is struck by the OBSERVER.*)

SCENE TWO

NARRATOR. (*Comes on, bows low, and speaks*) The little Lin Foo spent a happy and profitable day in the village. First he sold his basket of fritters and put the money in his trousers' pocket. Indeed, he had no trouble at all in selling the fritters, for the humble Wing Soong was known throughout the village for her fine cooking and fair bargains. The little lad went from booth to booth, finally deciding that the safest place for his money was under a stone near the entrance to the town. Then he could run and play to his heart's content, with no fear of the coins' slipping out of his pocket and rolling away in the dust. So, carefully he placed them there and joined some village boys he knew. Finally it was time to go home. He bade his friends farewell and went to the stone under which he had hidden his money. (*Bows and leaves Right*)

(*The OBSERVER strikes the GONG. The PROPERTY MAN places a stone in the center of the stage, saunters back to his chair, and sits. The MUSIC plays briefly, then subsides as LIN FOO enters.*)

LIN FOO. (*Enters Left and goes to the stone*) Now to put the money back into my pocket and go home before it is dark. (*Stoops and looks, but the money is not there*) Oh, my money! Where is it? All the coins that I put here are gone! Someone has stolen them while I played in the village. What will my mother, Wing Soong, do? She used all the money in our old stone crock to buy rice for the fritters! Oh dear, oh dear! (*Sits down and weeps*)

(*While the boy is sitting there weeping, the magistrate AN LI enters from the Left accompanied by his ATTENDANTS.*)

AN LI. Why are you weeping, my boy?

LIN FOO. Oh, Master, I am a poor boy whose mother makes fritters to sell on market day. She entrusted me to bring home the money which I placed under this stone for safekeeping. When I came to get it just now, I found it had been stolen. And so I have neither money nor fritters to take back with me!

AN LI. Have you a father, little Son?

LIN FOO. Oh, no, sir. There are just the two of us—my mother, Wing Soong, and I, who am called Lin Foo. We are very poor and must have what we earn at the market to live.

AN LI. Did you put the money well out of sight?

LIN FOO. Oh, yes, Honored Sir. No one could possibly have seen it.

AN LI. (*Pointing to it*) Is this the stone?

LIN FOO. It is, Your Honor.

AN LI. (*To his ATTENDANTS*) Then arrest this stone! You, my boy, may now go home. But don't fail to come back to this spot tomorrow morning. I shall try to get your money back for you.

LIN FOO. Yes, sir! Indeed, I shall!

AN LI. Now then, run along. It's growing late, and your mother will be worried.

LIN FOO. Oh, thank you! I shall be here in the morning. Good-by, Master. (*Runs in a circle, and out on the opposite side, Downstage Right*)

AN LI. (*Turning to his ATTENDANTS*) Summon all the villagers who were at the fair today to be present tomorrow morning. Let them be witnesses at the trial of this stone.

FIRST ATTENDANT. Yes, Your Honor.

AN LI. Bring with you also the magistrate's table and chair, two stout bamboo sticks, and a large stone jar.

SECOND ATTENDANT. Yes, Your Honor.

AN LI. That is all, then. You are dismissed.

(*ATTENDANTS bow low and leave the stage Right. AN LI steps forward and addresses the audience.*)

AN LI. I have been honored with the title Magistrate of this district. Since I have been in office, I have tried to perform my duties with justice and wisdom. This case is a most difficult one— for to prosecute a stone is impossible, and I am not yet certain as to how I shall find the stolen money for the poor Lin Foo and his widowed mother. In the morning I shall be watched by a hundred eyes! I must go home now to meditate upon this case. Tomorrow, most distinguished audience, we meet again. (*Bows low, exits Right*)

(*The OBSERVER strikes the GONG.*)

SCENE THREE

NARRATOR. (*Enters and bows*) It is the following day, and Wing Soong and her son have already left their cottage for the trial of the stone. As the magistrate commanded, the attendants have summoned all the villagers from the market place to act as witnesses. With your kind approval, ladies and gentlemen, the trial is about to begin. (*Bows and leaves Right*)

> (*The OBSERVER sounds the GONG. The MUSIC begins to play and the PROPERTY MAN is moving about, putting the stone in place, then the table and chair, and last of all, the bamboo sticks and jar. Into the jar he pours water, then retires to his table, where he is only occasionally interested in the proceedings. The VILLAGERS begin to enter and stand about in small groups. A few of them talk. WING SOONG and LIN FOO are in the crowd.*)

FIRST VILLAGER. They say the great An Li has sentenced a stone for the theft of some money.

SECOND VILLAGER. I think his mind is affected, and this is the proof of it.

> (*AN LI and his ATTENDANTS enter Upstage Left and the OBSERVER strikes the GONG. There is much ceremony as AN LI takes his place at the table. His ATTENDANTS stand one on each side of him.*)

THIRD VILLAGER. (*To his neighbor*) He looks all right. But one can never tell from appearances.

SECOND VILLAGER. Sh! He is about to speak.

AN LI. (*Bows and sits*) I have called all of you together this morning, my good friends, to act as witnesses at the trial of a stone. (*The VILLAGERS murmur*) Silence! Is the boy, Lin Foo, present?

LIN FOO. (*Stepping forward bashfully*) He is, Your Honor.

AN LI. And his mother, the widow, Wing Soong?

WING SOONG. (*Stepping forward*) She is, Your Honor.

AN LI. Did you, Wing Soong, give your son a basket of fritters to sell at the fair yesterday?

WING SOONG. Yes, Your Honor.

AN LI. And was the money for those fritters stolen from under the stone where he had hidden it?

WING SOONG. Oh, yes, Your Honor.

AN LI. (*Turning to the boy*) Was it this stone that stole the coins? (*As he points to the stone there is a ripple of amusement from the VILLAGERS*) Quiet!

LIN FOO. Yes, Your Honor.

AN LI. (*Turning to his ATTENDANTS*) Then will you strike the stone fifty times with the bamboo sticks?

(*Now the VILLAGERS laugh loudly, tapping their heads and showing ridicule, as the ATTENDANTS step forward and begin beating the stone.*)

AN LI. (*Suddenly shouting*) Silence! You are showing
contempt for this court! Each one of you shall
be fined twenty li, which you will toss into this
jar!

(*The VILLAGERS are sobered as they file past
the jar in a circle and drop in their coins. As*

the last man drops his in, AN LI jumps to his feet.)

AN LI. (*Shouting and pointing to the last man*) Arrest this man! He is the thief!

(*The VILLAGERS murmur in excitement and bewilderment.*)

FIRST VILLAGER. How does he know?

SECOND VILLAGER. The thief? Is he really the thief?

THIRD VILLAGER. He cannot tell!

(*There is general hubbub and exclamations among the VILLAGERS.*)

AN LI. (*Picking up the jar, which he brings forward, showing it to the VILLAGERS*) Do you see here? When this man dropped in his coin, these streaks of grease appeared on the surface of the water. Only *that* coin could have come from the basket that carried the fritters! (*To the THIEF*) Where is the rest of the money?

THIEF. (*Pulling it unwillingly from his pocket*) Here it is, Your Honor.

AN LI. Put it in the jar. (*THIEF does so*) Take him away. (*ATTENDANTS take him by both arms and they go off Upstage Right*) The court is dismissed!

(The VILLAGERS leave through both doors, expressing their amazement and respect for the magistrate's wisdom. All murmur softly until they are off the stage. Finally AN LI hands the jar to WING SOONG.)

AN LI. There you are, my good woman. Your money is restored to you, and I hope your son has learned his lesson—never to leave things of value foolishly in such a spot as this, thus tempting the dishonest folk who pass by to steal them.

WING SOONG. *(Taking the jar gratefully)* Oh, thank you, great Master. This humble servant now has twice as much money as the fritters would have brought.

AN LI. Then take it home and put it in safe-keeping. *(Claps his hands to the ATTENDANTS, who have just returned from Upstage Right)* Let us depart!

(AN LI and his ATTENDANTS exit Upstage Right. Both WING SOONG and LIN FOO bow low as they exit. They smile, sigh happily, and walk in a circle, then out in the direction of their cottage, Downstage Right. The OBSERVER strikes the GONG; the MUSIC begins to play loudly; and the CURTAINS close.)

A Tragic Story

There lived a sage in days of yore,
And he a handsome pigtail wore;
But wondered much and sorrowed more,
  Because it hung behind him.

He mused upon this curious case,
And swore he'd change the pigtail's place,
And have it hanging at his face,
  Not dangling there behind him.

Said he, "The mystery I've found—
I'll turn me round"—he turned him round,
  But still it hung behind him.

Then round and round, and out and in,
All day the puzzled sage did spin;
In vain—it mattered not a pin—
  The pigtail hung behind him.

And right and left, and roundabout,
And up and down and in and out
He turned; but still the pigtail stout
  Hung steadily behind him.

And though his efforts never slack,
And though he twist, and twirl, and tack,
Alas! still faithful to his back,
  The pigtail hangs behind him.

THE GREEN SONG

On the island of Puerto Rico are very little tree frogs, or coquis, as the islanders call them. They live in sugar cane fields and do the Green Work, singing the Green Song every evening. Coquis, so the story goes, believe the Green Song is responsible for keeping order in the heavens. It dusts the moon, polishes the stars, and sees to it that all goes well in the sky. The best singer of the Green Song was Pepe Coqui, the littlest coqui of all. One day Pepe is told that his sugar cane field is not the whole world, that the Green Song is not the only work of importance, and that green is not the only lovely color there is. Pepe cannot believe this; he has to see for himself. And so he sets off briskly for the airport, where this adventure begins.

Pepe traveled nearly all day, going through the green grass along the edges of the roads, and asking the way now and then from fellow coquis whom he met. By-and-by he came to the airport. He found the little window where a man was selling tickets. Suitcases and boxes were piled up like steps on one side of it and Pepe climbed and hopped up over these until he reached the counter in front of the window. "I want to buy a ticket. I am going to New York," he said.

"Get in line," said the Ticket Seller.

"Where is that?" Pepe asked.

"Get behind the last person waiting there," and the Ticket Seller pointed out the place for Pepe.

Pepe hopped to the place and waited. Soon the person ahead of him stepped forward a little way, and so did Pepe. "I am going to New York," Pepe told him. But the person said nothing. He just stood there in line.

"Perhaps he didn't hear me," Pepe thought and he shouted louder. This time the person turned but then, after looking around a second, he turned back.

"I am down here!" Pepe yelled.

The person looked down, and sure enough, he saw Pepe. "Why, it's a coqui!" he exclaimed.

"Naturally, I'm a coqui," Pepe said proudly. "I am going to New York."

"Don't tell me that!" the person said. "Don't tell me that coquis are leaving the Island and going to New York!"

"Not the coquis. Only me. I'm Pepe Coqui. Only I am going."

The person seemed to feel better. "Oh, then it's all right. We cannot do without our coquis."

"Of course not," Pepe agreed.

"Are you looking for work?" the person asked politely.

"*Looking* for work? I have my own work. It is the Green Work, of course."

"And you can do it anywhere?"

"Naturally. I am a coqui." Pepe drew himself up to his tallest height.

"How lucky you are! Now I am going to New York to look for work." At that moment the Ticket Seller called and the person left Pepe.

And then, next, it was Pepe's turn. He hopped up on the counter. "Now just what *is* a ticket?" he asked the man.

The Ticket Seller pushed his spectacles up on his forehead and looked at Pepe carefully. "A ticket," he said, "is a piece of paper that shows you have bought a seat on the plane."

"What can I do with the seat after I buy it?"

"You can sit on it."

"Oh, you mean a chair!" Pepe said. "How big is this chair?"

"It's a seat, and it's that big." The Ticket Seller pointed to a chair in the office where he stood.

"Well, that," said Pepe, "is a chair. Are you sure you understand about these matters?"

"Of course I understand! A chair can be a seat!"

"I am not sure that you do. For instance, anyone could see that that chair is too big for me."

"Who cares?" The Ticket Seller began to shout.

Pepe was astonished. "Why, I do! And what if I fell off? And then, too, there is the matter of the cost."

"The cost is the same for every seat."

"Even if one only sat on a corner of it?"

"Nobody sits on a corner of it! A seat is for one person! It fits one person!"

"It doesn't fit me. Look!"

Pepe hopped down from the counter and sat on the seat inside the office. The ticket man had to put his spectacles back on to see him because he

was so small and the chair was so big. The ticket man scratched his head. "How could we strap you in it?" he asked.

"Strap me?"

"Everyone must have a strap around him to hold him safely when the plane flies off the ground."

"In that case, I most certainly require a seat my size," Pepe told him with dignity.

"Just a minute," the Ticket Seller said. "You wait here and I will come back." He went out of his office holding his head in his hands. He went to the office of his chief, and threw himself into a chair.

"I have a coqui in my office," he told the chief.

"Oh, that's all right," the chief answered. "They don't bite, you know. Or sting, or anything ugly like that."

"But this one wants to buy a ticket to New York."

The chief's eyes brightened. "Well, sell him one."

"He won't buy a regular one. He says the seat is too big. And there is something to what he says. The seat looks much bigger when he sits on it."

"Hmmmmm," said the chief. "I'd better look into this. This is the first time a coqui has asked for a ticket. We'd better take good care of him. He is the first, but he may not be the last." The chief laughed and patted the Ticket Seller on the back cheerfully.

The two went back to the Ticket Seller's office where Pepe was waiting. He was still sitting in the middle of the big seat. "How do you do, sir?" the chief greeted him.

"Very well, I thank you," Pepe replied. "Except in the matter of a seat to go on my visit to the world."

"Hmmm," said the chief. "It is a little roomy, isn't it? And you are going to visit the world, you say?"

"Oh, yes."

"You want a round-the-world ticket, I suppose?"

"No, I want a New York ticket."

"No doubt he will go in stages," the chief whispered to the Ticket Seller. "New York first, you know. Good service may persuade him to travel farther with our company." Then aloud he said, "Now let's see what we can do about the proper seat for you. Hmmmmm. I will call *my* chief."

The chief called his chief, and this chief called the first vice-president, who called two more vice-presidents who decided it was a matter for the Traffic Manager. The Traffic Manager thought it should be taken care of by the captain and officers of the plane. They talked a while and then the engineer said, "I think I will be able to fix it. Yes, indeed. How big is he?"

"He's not very big," the Ticket Seller said. "About this big." He measured a space in the air with his hands.

"Oh, no," said his chief. "He's *this* big." And he, too, measured the air with his hands.

"I will have to measure him myself," said the engineer. He took a ruler and went in where Pepe was still waiting.

"It is getting rather late," Pepe said.

"Yes, indeed," the engineer replied. "Would you be good enough to sit on this ruler, please?"

"Why?"

"To see what your size is."

"I am the smallest of the coquis."

"But I must know your size exactly. I am the engineer."

By now Pepe was expecting things to be strange, so, although no one had ever before asked him to sit on a ruler, he hopped over and tried to sit on this one. It was not an easy thing to do because the ruler was made of shiny wood and was not only hard but slippery as well. Pepe slid down from it a few times but finally he got a good grip on it with his feet and sat down. The engineer was standing behind him. "Is this the way?" Pepe called over his shoulder.

"Yes, indeed," the engineer said. He looked down at Pepe on the ruler. "Well, now, let me see. It seems that you are almost an inch in size."

"I am?" Pepe was pleased. "That's a very fine size, I suppose?"

"Oh, yes, indeed. I think that now we can fix a seat that will be just right."

"Well, I hope so. I am going to cross the water that has the new words in it."

"What new words?"

"Well, I cannot remember them now, but when I see them I will know. That's why I'm going to visit the world."

"Excuse me," said the engineer and ran out of the office.

The Ticket Seller came back. "The engineer seems to be in a hurry," he said.

"He's hurrying to fix my seat. I told him it was getting late," Pepe informed him.

"Well, now that everything is settled, please make yourself comfortable. Your seat will be ready for the next plane, and they are having a talk about the price of your ticket."

"Will the price be according to size?" Pepe asked him.

"Well, yes."

"In that case," Pepe told him, "the price will be almost an inch."

"Almost an inch of what?"

"That is my size. I am almost an inch. I sat on the ruler."

"We don't sell tickets like that!"

"Like what?"

"By the inch!" the Ticket Seller shouted.

"You said it was according to size—"

"It is—but not like that! Money doesn't come by inches!"

"Well, you said the ticket would be by size, and as I told you, *that*," Pepe said firmly, "is almost an inch. Then I will measure the money to that."

Once again the Ticket Seller ran out of his office holding his head in his hands. He went into the room where the two chiefs and the three vice-presidents were holding their meeting. They looked at him, surprised.

"There is no reason for any of you to think about this problem any longer," he told them. "He—" and the Ticket Seller pointed to his office—"has got it all settled."

"Why, that's fine," said the first vice-president.

"Just a minute. Who has got it all settled?" asked the second one, who had been dozing.

"The coquí! The one in my office! The ticket is to be according to size—his size—which, he says over and over, is almost an inch!"

"Be calm," said the third vice-president. "We must face this bravely."

"Hmmmm," said the Ticket Seller's chief, "this is a new idea."

"And I don't think much of it," the second vice-president added.

"It may be the right answer, and again it may not be," said the first vice-president. "Let's go in and talk to him."

When they came into the office Pepe greeted them politely. "What can I do for you?" he asked.

"Well, it's about this ticket," the first vice-president began.

"Didn't the Ticket Seller explain to you?" Pepe asked in surprise.

"Yes, but how, exactly, would it work?"

"That is what *I* would like to know," said Pepe. "Here is the ruler. Now you measure a ticket, almost an inch size, you know."

The men nodded to the Ticket Seller. His hands trembled as he put the ticket on the ruler. "I never thought I would be doing anything like this," he said. "Here, this is almost an inch."

"Well, cut that off," Pepe explained patiently.

The Ticket Seller cut off the ticket and gave it to Pepe. Pepe held up a dollar bill. He measured the bill to the ticket. "Almost an inch is not quite a quarter of a dollar," he said in a pleasant voice.

The Ticket Seller jumped. "It is not enough money!"

"It's according to size," Pepe told them all.

"I think," said the first vice-president, "we had better let it go for the moment. Later, we can have many talks and decide about the regular price of coqui tickets."

The others thought the first vice-president's words were very wise. They nodded to each other, breathed a sigh of relief, and the Ticket Seller gave the ticket to Pepe. Pepe gave him the money. Then each of the men bowed to Pepe. "We hope you have a pleasant trip," they said, one by one, as they left.

"I hope so, too," Pepe answered.

In the plane the carpenters worked on Pepe's seat. They put it on one side of the wall, near a window. Then they made a safety belt and put it around the seat. When it was all finished the engineer went to the ticket office to tell Pepe that his plane was ready to go.

The Latin word *officium* means "performance of duty." Through the years this has changed to the French form which was adopted in English as **office**. An office is usually thought of as a place in which one works rather than the work itself.

The Object Comes to Life

In her poem "A Summer Morning," Rachel Field expressed herself in this way:

I saw dawn creep across the sky,
And all the gulls go flying by.
I saw the sea put on its dress
Of blue mid-summer loveliness,
And heard the trees begin to stir
Great arms of pine and juniper.
I heard the wind call out and say:
"Get up, my dear, it is to-day!"

When writing the above lines, the poet painted a word picture of a summer morning by giving life-like characteristics to nonliving things. In line 1 the poet says that the dawn *creeps*. Then in line 3 she tells about the sea *putting on its dress*. In this way the poet helps you build mental images while you are reading. What other personal characteristics has Rachel Field given to lifeless things in the above poem?

Writers of poetry and descriptive prose frequently use this method. It is an extremely effective means of communication because it creates sensory images in your mind.

In what ways can <u>you</u> paint word pictures by giving lifelike characteristics to nonliving things?

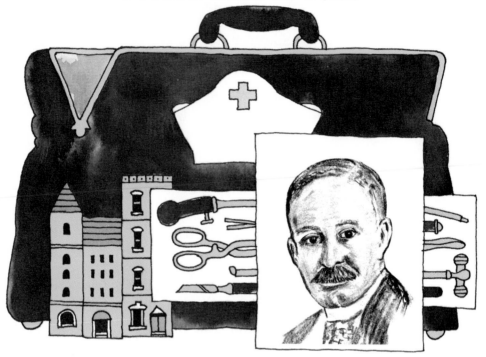

Daniel Hale Williams: Surgeon

The ticket agent at the Annapolis, Maryland, railroad station studied the ten-year-old black boy as he listened to his story. The boy lived with a family in Annapolis, he said, but was lonesome for his mother and six brothers and sisters who had moved to Janesville, Wisconsin. He had bundled up his clothes and come down to take the train to Janesville.

"A ticket to Wisconsin costs a lot of money," the agent reminded him.

"I don't have any money," the boy replied.

"It's a long trip for a young fellow like you," the agent warned.

"I can make it all right," said the boy.

Did the agent recognize something special in ten-year-old Daniel Hale Williams? Perhaps so, for with great kindness he wrote out a pass and the young traveler soon was on his way.

Daniel went to school in Janesville, then was apprenticed to a shoemaker, a barber, a lawyer, and finally to a doctor. The latter helped him to enter the medical school at Northwestern University, from which he graduated in 1883. He helped pay his way through college by playing in orchestras on the excursion boats that went from Chicago to Milwaukee.

The young doctor opened an office on the south side of Chicago, and divided his time between his medical practice and teaching at Northwestern. He was greatly concerned that no hospitals in his adopted city permitted Negro doctors on their staffs. Because of this, operations had to be performed in the homes of Negro patients. And there was no proper training available for Negro nurses.

To correct this unfair situation, young Dr. Williams established Provident Hospital in 1891. At Provident, doctors of any race were welcome. Here, too, was created the first training school for Negro nurses in this country.

It was at Provident that Daniel Hale Williams attained world-wide fame by performing the first successful heart operation in the history of medicine. A young man, bleeding badly, was brought into the emergency ward. On examining him, Dr. Williams found that he had been stabbed in the heart. It seemed certain that he would die, but the doctor decided to do something no one had ever done— operate on the heart.

With amazing daring and unbelievable skill, he cut the walls of the heart, sewed up the wound, and then closed the walls while the heart continued beating. The "impossible operation" had been done successfully, and overnight Williams became one of the most famous doctors in the country.

The next year President Grover Cleveland asked him to become the head of the new Freedman's Hospital in Washington. Williams accepted and again proved himself a great organizer. He established a training school there for black nurses and aided young black doctors who were discriminated against in the national capital. Returning to Chicago, he continued his brilliant record as a surgeon. He was made a fellow of the American College of Surgeons, a high honor for a doctor. The boy in the Annapolis station had gone a long way. When Williams died in 1931, he had been a famous doctor for almost forty years.

Malvina Hoffman: Sculptress

The tropical sun was so hot Malvina Hoffman took some banana leaves from the jungle, dipped them in water, and placed them in her hat. It was the only way she could be refreshed and continue her work of modeling the head of a Sakai tribesman in the Malayan peninsula. He had agreed to pose for Miss Hoffman if other members of her party would walk out of sight with the other Sakais and leave them alone in the jungle for two hours.

She had convinced him that her sculptor's knife had a dull blade and was not a weapon. Now she wanted to convince him that he should put his sharp steel-blade knife back into its sheath. By means of eye and sign language movements, she asked him to lend her his knife. As she began to draw the sharp blade over her arm, he shook his head wildly and, taking back his knife, pushed it into its sheath for the first time since they had met. Miss Hoffman grasped his hand and shook it firmly as they both started to smile and laugh.

Watching very closely as she made her preparations to begin her work, he seemed to understand what was expected of him. Frequent interruptions were caused by a group of gibbons that climbed out on the branches of nearby trees and pelted Miss Hoffman with bananas and laughed at her efforts. Her Sakai friend took care of the gibbons with some carefully aimed poison arrows shot into the trees, making them quickly disperse.

This open-air sculpture was part of the work Malvina Hoffman was doing for the Chicago Field Museum. The trustees of the Museum had decided to make an exhibit showing the many different people of the world. They wanted the figures to be as lifelike as possible. This was an assignment which would mean a great deal of hard work and require an artist of exceptional skill. Because Miss Hoffman had these qualities, she was asked to do the work.

Malvina Hoffman grew up in a home where music and other forms of art were a central part of family life. Her parents encouraged her to train and develop her talent, and she studied sculpturing in America and in Europe. Determined to learn all phases of her profession, she became a medical student and studied the structure of the human body in great detail. She visited foundries to learn every step in the casting of bronze, and she became adept in handling the carpenter's and plumber's tools used in building the core around which the clay figure is shaped. Miss Hoffman won recognition for her ability and received many awards and honors.

Her work for the Field Museum took her to far-off strange parts of the world. She traveled by comfortable ships, swinging camel caravans, rickshaws, and even rode a royal elephant in India. Her living accommodations ranged from palaces to thatched-roof huts with rice-paper walls.

At the completion of her project, when the models had been cast in bronze and finishing processes applied, they were shipped to the Field Museum in Chicago. The exhibit in the Hall of Man was opened to the public in June, 1933.

As a young girl, Malvina's father once said to her, "Above all, you must be an artist. Then you can create art." By putting her whole mind and heart at the service of her great talent she followed her father's advice and left for the world her view of life in beautiful and lasting form.

Edward Cliff: Conservationist

The people around Murderer's Creek in eastern Oregon couldn't believe their ears. That young fellow from the Forest Service was telling them to hunt *more* deer. That just didn't make sense.

But as Edward Cliff continued to explain why more mule deer should be hunted, people began to change their minds. "There are too many deer for the food supply," stated Cliff. "Because of this, you'll have to change your hunting laws to allow more deer to be hunted. If you don't, many deer will starve to death next year. The deer left will destroy valuable young trees and shrubs by over-eating the leaves, twigs, and stems."

This wasn't the first time Edward Cliff had to educate people about the proper management of wildlife and forests. This had been his job since graduating from Utah State University in 1931. And this job would continue when he became Chief of the United States Forest Service in 1962.

Soon after developing good game management practices around Murderer's Creek, Cliff was called on to tackle an even more serious problem. In 1939 the people around the Siskiyou National Forest in Oregon were continually setting fires in the National Forest. Cliff and his crew of rangers decided that the only solution was to teach the people good conservation practices.

It was true that the mountaineers could pasture livestock on the land and farm some of it, once the trees were burned off. But soon the land would become badly eroded by wind and water. Some men burned forest areas to open the forest for hunting, but the fires usually killed off most of the game.

By working closely with the people, Cliff was able to convince them that the forest fires were doing much more harm than good. The next year there was a sharp drop in the number of fires set by arsonists. During the third year of the program none of the fires in the Siskiyou National Forest was man-made in origin.

Cliff's talents were used continuously in the field and in the national offices of the Forest Service in Washington, D.C. In 1944 Cliff was called to Washington to serve as assistant to the Chief of the Division of Range Management. In 1946 he went to the Intermountain Region at Ogden, Utah; then he became Regional Forester in the Rocky Mountain Region, with headquarters in Denver. He was recalled to Washington in 1952 and has remained there ever since. In 1962 he was made Chief of Forest Service.

Today, Edward Cliff continues to use his knowledge of game and plant management as he directs the many activities of the Forest Service. As manager of 187,000,000 acres of national forests and national grasslands, Cliff knows how important it is to preserve the animals and forests of America. He relies heavily upon the skill and the training of 21,000 permanent employees and as many more part-time employees as he continues his fight for conservation of natural resources. One of the outstanding scientist-workers in America today is conservationist Edward Cliff.

---

1. How did each person use his or her skills to benefit all men?

2. What do you think all three had in common? Explain your answer.

3. Which of the three professions mentioned would you like to follow? Why?

The Greek word *bios*, meaning "life," has been combined with the Greek root *graph*, meaning "to write," to form the word **biography.** A biography is a written account of someone's life.

Add a Little Flavor to Your Writing

Just for a moment, imagine that you are living in a world where everything is alike. Buildings are of the same design and are painted the same color. People, all dressed alike, and having a similar attitude toward life, move along identical streets at the same pace. You are living in a homogenized world. What a dull place to live!

You know, though, that fortunately life is not like that. Life has form, color, sound, taste, odor, and feeling. And because life is so varied, exciting, and vivid, most writers—like painters at their easels —use lights, darks, and contrasts in giving their impressions to others. Often writers try to help you understand their ideas by using *comparison*. A truly good writer searches for the unusual picture to make you see exactly what he sees. His most effective tool is *figurative language*, which adds flavor to writing. Use of words in this unusual way helps to form a sharp picture in the reader's mind by making an interesting comparison—a seeing of one thing in terms of another. Instead of merely describing the kitchen refrigerator as "making a humming noise," the poet James Tate expresses it in this way:

> Like a glum cricket
> the refrigerator is singing.

What mental image of Lincoln do you have when you read these words by John Gould Fletcher?

Like a gaunt, scraggly pine
Which lifts its head above the mournful sandhills;

Notice that the previous selections introduced the comparisons with the word *like*. Sometimes the word *as* is used to introduce the comparison. Frequently, though, writers make a comparison with a statement that sounds as if it were the actual fact, as in these lines by Barbara Howes:

My cat, washing her tail's tip, is a whorl
Of white shell.

In that example, the comparison does not contain the words *like* or *as*.

In the following selection, Ethel Romig Fuller says that something IS actually something else:

Wind is a cat
That prowls at night.

Notice how Patricia Hubbell describes night:

Night is a purple pumpkin
Laced with a silver web.

Often, when trying to describe things, you will observe carefully. Good observation leads to good writing. So when you write, add flavor with comparisons that will help the reader to build mental images.

GAY-NECK AND HIS FOLLOWERS

One day Swift, the crow, saw a hunter approaching to trap birds. Swift decided to follow along to warn the other animals that a hunter was present.

Now the hunter picked a spot, spread a snare, scattered grain, and hid close by. But the birds who lived in the woods were warned by Swift's loud cries and did not take any of the rice grains placed as bait.

At this time a dove king named Gay-Neck, with hundreds of his followers, was wandering in search of food. He spied the grain and in spite of Swift's warnings, flew down to eat and landed in the snare. Gay-Neck and his followers were trapped.

The hunter gleefully lifted his club and ran forward. Then Gay-Neck and the other doves became frightened. But the king gained his senses and said: "Have no fear, my friends. We must all agree in purpose and fly up in unison. That way we will carry the snare away with us. As the saying goes:

> Bharunda birds will teach you why
> The disunited have cause to cry;
> For, single-bellied, double-necked,
> They took a diet incorrect."

"How was that?" asked the doves. And Gay-Neck told the story of the Bharunda Birds.

By a certain lake in the world lived birds called "bharunda birds." They had one belly and two necks apiece.

While one of these birds was wandering about, his first neck found some fine nectar. Then the second said: "Give me half." And then when the first neck refused, the second neck picked up some green fruit and ate it. As they had one belly, they became very ill and neither one could eat for a long time.

"And that is why I say:

> Bharunda birds will teach you why
> The disunited have cause to cry;
> For single-bellied, double-necked,
> They took a diet incorrect.

Through united action there is strength."

When the doves heard this, and being eager to live awhile longer, they united their efforts to carry the snare away. They all flew an arrowshot into the air, formed together, and proceeded without fear.

When the hunter saw the snare fly away, he
looked up in amazement and said:

> So long as they agree, they may
> Carry the fatal snare away;
> But they will quickly disagree,
> And then those birds belong to me.

With this in mind, he started to pursue.

Gay-Neck saw the hunter's plan and flew over
such rough land that the hunter was forced to turn
back. Then Gay-Neck turned to his followers and

said: "See! We may travel quietly now for the hunter has been overcome by our efforts. We will now fly to a distant city in which a mouse named Gold lives. He is a friend of mine and will cut our bonds in a hurry."

And so Gay-Neck led his followers to the home of Gold. After they were set free, the doves were a little more careful about which fields of grain they chanced to land in for their meals.

 The Medieval Latin word *unisonus* meant "singing the same sound" or "singing in harmony." Today you might sing in **unison** or, more commonly, you might work in harmony with others.

THE FUTURE OF SPACESHIP EARTH

Let's imagine the earth as a tiny spaceship traveling through the universe, carrying with it its own limited resources for maintaining life. What we have now is all we will ever have to keep us alive.

Above us is a narrow band of usable atmosphere, no more than seven miles high, with no "new" air available to us. Beneath us exists a crust of land with only one-eighth of the surface fit for human life. And around us we find a limited supply of "usable" water that we must constantly cleanse and reuse.

Together and without man's interference—land, air, and water work well together. There is a ceaseless exchange of materials and of energy between living things and their environment. The system follows a circular pathway which is repeated in endless cycles. These cycles maintain the great chain of life and the delicate balance of nature, from ocean depth to mountain top. A thin skin of soil, water, and air covers the earth's surface. The presence of plants and animals living within this covering is proof that their living area, or *environment*, is suitable to support life as we know it.

As scientists think about the future, they worry about the problem of overpopulation. Across the earth, the number of people is increasing at a faster rate than the amount of food produced. Even in

the food-rich United States, huge surpluses no longer exist. Some food experts predict that widespread starvation and eventually wars for food will halt the population growth. Man has destroyed much of the earth's food-producing lands. For centuries, the Americans have unwisely converted the thin forest soils to cropland or have overgrazed animals on grasslands which have become eroded and therefore yield soil unable to reseed itself. Unless population growth is slowed and the food supply greatly increased, world starvation may occur.

Another problem that worries scientists is man's misuse of *technology* (the materials and machines that man makes and uses). Constantly man discovers that the changes brought about by technology cause other unexpected changes on the spaceship Earth. For example, by using chemical poisons to help control the insect pests that spread disease and eat crops, man also destroys birds, fish, and other valuable animals. By using fertilizers, farmers have greatly increased the quantity of food that can be grown on a plot of land. Yet, chemicals from fertilizers wash off the land and affect the life in ponds and lakes. And, although the automobile is considered necessary for travel in many parts of the world, the wastes from autos now choke the air of cities around the world.

The United States, the wealthiest country on spaceship Earth, has special problems with its technology. U. S. industries use materials from all over the world. But most of these industry-made products are used, then thrown away. Each year in the United States, people throw away more than 200,000 tons of aluminum, tin, lead, and zinc and three million tons of iron. Some of these metals are recovered and used again. However, many tons of the earth's metals are being thrown into dumps, streams, junkyards, and along roadsides.

The America of which we sing:

> Oh, beautiful for spacious skies,
> For amber waves of grain;
> For purple mountain majesties
> Above the fruited plain . . .

the America we inherited—this America is quickly becoming the country whose "spacious skies" are filled with factory soot, with strong smelling chemicals, and poisonous gases. Many of its "amber waves of grain" have been replaced by clouds of dust, and its "purple mountain majesties" stand amid the stumps of cut trees or charred ruins of burnt forests. Several of the "fruited plains" are now gullied by erosion and washed away into rivers, which have become murky and scummy because of pollution. This is the America we have *made*.

It is true that mountains have been moved, huge cities built, deserts have been made to bloom, and now man has begun his reach into space and its unexplored territories. But man still depends on earth's air, water, soil, and other resources. Our growing numbers of people must learn to take better care of the limited supplies aboard the spaceship Earth. There is no other choice, because it is the *only* Earth we have!

1. Why do scientists worry about overpopulation when they think about the future?
2. In what ways is man misusing technology?
3. What kind of health problems can result from polluted air?

 Natural **resources** provide supplies that can be used when needed. The original Latin form and a later French form meant "to rise again." Do you think factories would be able "to rise again" if natural resources are not preserved?

The Coin

Into my heart's treasury
   I slipped a coin
That time cannot take
   Nor a thief purloin,—
Oh, better than the minting
   Of a gold-crowned king
Is the safe-kept memory
   Of a lovely thing.

TREASURE AT WILDCAT GLEN

Just a few days more of summer vacation and then Katie John Tucker and her friend Edwin Jones would be back in school. So, as a last "fling" for the summer, Katie John persuaded Edwin to take her to Wildcat Glen. According to the stories around town, a wildcat had once lived in this wooded spot and that's how it got its name.

As they pedaled along on their bikes, Edwin told Katie John about the magazine article he'd been reading on undersea archeology.

"Just think," Edwin exclaimed. "They might find sunken Roman galleys. Find out all kinds of stuff about ancient trade routes on the seas."

Katie John thought about Edwin and his archeology and asked curiously, "How come you aren't crazy about exploring space like the other boys are?"

"They want to see where we're going. I want to see where we've been, that's all."

"It's just as much of a mystery, isn't it?"

Edwin corrected her. "Not *just* as much. Quite a bit is known about the past. But there's lots more to find out."

They pedaled along, discussing the article. Presently the road dipped low near the river, and they were at Wildcat Glen. The creek of the glen ran under a small bridge in the road and on down to the river. Katie John and Edwin dragged their bikes into some bushes, walked into the hollow, and set off up the glen along the creek.

The creek bed led them into an open field on a hill overlooking the Mississippi. In the field was a weathered gray farmhouse. Edwin and Katie raced through the tall grass and stood on the porch steps of the house.

"This place looks deserted," Edwin said.

There was no doubt about it. The house was dead. Katie and Edwin walked into the front room. Streaked no-color wallpaper hung in torn strips from the walls. Some floorboards were broken through, and there were shotgun shells scattered about as if hunters had stopped there. Only one of the windows still had glass in it. And yet, the house wasn't completely bare. There were still some ancient furnishings about. A large old heating stove stood in the front room, its stovepipe gone, and along one wall sagged a long, old-fashioned couch. Springs stuck up out of holes, and the upholstery was chewed bare in spots.

"That certainly doesn't look comfortable." Katie John plumped herself down on the couch, and a whoosh of dust rose from it.

"Look out," Edwin warned. "You may be sitting on a nest of mice."

She got up hastily, and followed Edwin, who had already gone into the next room.

"There are still some things in the kitchen, too," Edwin called.

Katie John ran to look. Sure enough, in the big kitchen was an old iron cookstove, a table, a sink with a hand pump in it, a high-backed rocking chair.

"Here's a book," Edwin reported. "A *Farmer's Almanac*, 1925."

As Katie looked up she noticed something on the wall by the stove. "Here's a calendar."

She studied it and noticed that the pages were torn off to July, 1932.

"Edwin, you know what this means!" Katie exclaimed. "Whoever lived here left in July, 1932. Nobody's lived here since."

"They could have left before July," Edwin said. "Hunters could have torn off pages since."

"But the family was here sometime in 1932," Katie insisted, "or they wouldn't have hung up the calendar then."

"Yes, and look at these clippings."

Articles and pictures cut from newspapers and magazines were tacked all over the wall above the sink. Edwin ran his finger over them, hunting for dates on the papers. He and Katie found several. The latest one seemed to be February 4, 1932.

"It certainly looks as though they were here until 1932," Katie said. "But why did they leave things behind? Of course, most of it is junk, but you'd think they'd take that rocker and the almanac."

"You know, Katie John," Edwin said slowly, "maybe the family left even more stuff than is here now. It looks as if this place has been deserted for more than thirty years. People could have carted off a lot of things in that time."

"You mean—they could have just picked up and left suddenly—left everything?" Katie felt strangely

frightened by the idea. "Do you suppose they all were eaten by the wildcat?"

Edwin laughed one of his rare out-loud laughs, breaking up the lonely feeling. "Oh, Katie, you and your nutty ideas! That wildcat would have popped! Come on, let's see what's in the barn."

There wasn't much of interest in the barn, so Katie John and Edwin decided that the upstairs of the house, yet unexplored, might hold better possibilities. There was even less of interest in the bedrooms than in the barn, however. They were quite bare.

Katie John opened every door, and at last in one bedroom she came upon a low door the height of a four-year-old. She tugged it open and found a small closet under the sloping roof of the house. She crawled into it. The shut-up air was hot and stuffy and it was dark in there, but then she spied something.

"Edwin, a box!"

The carton was heavy as she shoved it out into the bedroom for more light.

"Oh, just magazines. Still, I wonder what kind of magazines they read?"

She lifted them out. There were old copies of women's magazines and *National Geographic*. The cover pictures looked more and more old-fashioned as she dug deeper into the box.

"That's all," she said, taking out the last magazine.

And there at the bottom was the treasure: a small narrow box, and inside, a fan. The ivory handle was carved out in a lacy design and a ring of ivory hung from the handle. Carefully Katie John spread open the fan, and the silk, though yellowed with age, didn't crack.

"How lovely!" she breathed.

And how strange to find something so delicately beautiful in a tumble-down old farmhouse.

"Do you suppose I could have it?"

"If you want." Edwin shrugged. "Everybody else has taken what they wanted from here. Though that fan sure doesn't go with your pigtails."

"Huh! I guess I can take my hair *out* of pigtails if I like."

Katie John started to put the magazines back into the carton, and then she noticed something else in the bottom, a small square of hard paper. She turned it over and saw that it was a picture of a young woman, showing just her head and shoulders. It was a very old photograph in fading brown. The girl wore a high-necked blouse, and her hair swirled around her head, held back by a wide band. Katie John studied the photograph. This girl's face was small and came to a pointed chin. And what were those spots under her eyes? Freckles!

"Edwin, look." Katie showed it to him, laughing without knowing why. "I like her."

Edwin stared at the photograph, then smiled. "You know why? She sort of looks like you."

Katie John looked at the picture again. "Oh, I don't know. I just think she looks friendly."

Slowly Katie John put the picture back in the bottom of the box and stacked the magazines on top of it. The fan and the picture surely were from the early 1900's, long before the 1930's, the date on the calendar downstairs. Had the family lived in this house for generations, the way Katie's ancestors had in Great-Aunt Emily's house?

Edwin had gone back downstairs, and Katie followed him, carrying the fan box. She found Edwin examining the front-door frame. He pointed to the top of the frame. Twisting her head, she read, "Calkins, 1910."

"I thought I'd find it here," Edwin said. "In the old days a builder often carved his name and the date of building somewhere on the house."

Katie asked if it was the name of the builder or the family who owned the house, but Edwin wasn't sure.

"We've just got to find out more about who lived here. I know! The newspaper clippings. Maybe they're wedding stories, birth announcements, sort of a family history in clippings."

She and Edwin ran back to the kitchen. However, the clippings didn't seem to have anything personal about a family.

"Let's ask about this place when we get back to town," Katie John said. "Surely somebody in Barton's Bluff will know the story of this place."

"Katie, no!" Edwin's usually cool face blazed with excitement. "I've got it! Let's study this place the way archeologists would. We'll find out who this family was all on our own."

Archeologists learned how ancient peoples lived by digging up things the people left behind, he reminded Katie. Sometimes they'd find old walls, and they'd dig trenches, hunting for things such as old pottery and tools, things that would tell what the people were like, how they'd lived.

"And we don't even have to dig," Edwin said. "All sorts of clues are left here—the date on the door, the calendar, the clippings, the fan, the stuff in the barn. Everything's a clue. Bit by bit, we'll piece things together."

The afternoon had a very late feeling by now, and Katie and Edwin decided they'd better go home.

Edwin insisted on following the grassy ruts that led away from it. The path—you couldn't call it a road any more—curved away through the woods, and there were even young saplings growing up in it. Edwin said they could try to figure the age of these little trees and so get some idea of how long it had been since the road had been used. Before long the path came out on the Wildcat Glen road, not far beyond where they'd left their bikes.

Katie John placed the fan box in her bicycle basket. Pedaling back to town, she thought of the treasure she was carrying home. And then she wondered, why had the freckle-faced girl no longer wanted or needed her fan? Why had she left it behind?

August melted into September, school opened, and with its opening came all kinds of problems for Katie John. Unthinkingly she announced that she hated boys—all boys, that is, except Edwin. Then the other boys began teasing Edwin about being a "pretty girly-girl" because he was a friend of the boy-hater, Katie.

Finally one afternoon Edwin had had all he could take from them. He whirled at Katie John, his face white with rage, and shouted, "From now on, stay away from me, you hear!"

It was a Saturday morning in early October when Katie John realized that she had to go back to Wildcat Glen. She didn't quite understand why, but she just *had* to find out about the girl and the fan.

The glen was as quiet as before. Katie scrambled up a bank and through the trees. Yes, there was the old gray farmhouse still, just as it had been there since—when was it?—1910.

Now to study all the details, begin reconstructing the life there. First, the surroundings of the house.

What kind of flowers had the ladies of the house liked and planted? She turned the corner. What was this little thing? A little wild rosebush!

"How very old are you, bush?" she said to the wild rose. "Did someone love you?"

Had the freckled girl planted the wild rose so long ago?

Before Katie did anything else, she wanted to see the picture again. She ran into the house and up the stairs. Pulling the carton out of the closet, she dumped out the magazines. Ah, the picture. Katie John held it in her fingers.

"Who are you?" she said.

The girl-woman didn't smile. She was properly serious for this occasion of having her photograph taken. But there were points of light in her eyes, like a sparkle. And that nose and those freckles could never look serious, Katie thought. Without smiling, the girl looked happy. And pretty.

Katie began figuring. If this house was built in 1910, and this girl looked like the pictures of girls in the magazines of the early 1900's, then maybe this house was built for her. Maybe she'd come here as a bride! Immediately Katie John knew she was going to work on this theory. The girl had become the lady of this house, and she'd learn about the girl from studying the house.

Perhaps that wasn't the scientific way. Did archeologists have a theory about scientific civilizations when they started digging? And then did they watch to see if the pots and things they found fitted their theory about the people who'd lived there? She wasn't sure.

"But that's the way I'm going to do it!"

Now, what sort of person was the girl? She'd had cheeks like speckled eggs and a merry look despite her serious lips. How did a girl who looked so honest and everyday fit with a fan that looked like moonlight, music, romance? How had she become a woman who'd used the fan? For that matter, maybe the fan didn't even belong to her. Yet the picture and the fan were together. Katie John was sure they belonged to each other.

Well, she could start with the magazines. What did the girl read? On the cover of one of the magazines was a drawing of a man and a lady dancing. "Romance and Social Number" the cover read. The date was February 1, 1911. Katie turned the pages, thinking of the girl reading the love stories.

Katie John decided to give the girl a name, at least until she found out what her name really was. She knew that wasn't at all scientific, but it was too vague to keep calling her "the girl, the woman, the lady." A nice, old-fashioned name— Netta. Somehow, that had to be the girl's name.

Maybe her name was on address stickers on the magazines! Katie hunted through all the magazines, but none of the covers had stickers on them. Oh well, perhaps magazines weren't mailed with stickers back in those days.

Katie John leafed through the magazines—old issues of ladies' magazines and *Boy's Life*. *Boy's Life*? Those were more recent, in the 1920's.

Aha! then boys had lived here. A discovery! Netta had had at least one son!

Katie John reviewed what she'd found. A lady who'd owned a fan lived here, and there'd been at least one boy. Surely a husband, too? Were there daughters? The magazines didn't seem to be able to tell her anything more. She put them back in the box, but she kept the picture of the girl, placing it carefully in her pocket.

Katie went downstairs. In the front room there was nothing but the broken-down couch and the big stove. The dining room had nothing to offer but a built-in china cabinet with broken glass panes. Katie dragged the rocker in from the kitchen to stand on it to look at the top shelf. Nothing. Oh, why hadn't the family left something forgotten and interesting on the top shelf?

Still, she wasn't discouraged. The kitchen held the most possibilities, and she'd been saving it for last.

A woman spends most of her time in the kitchen, she reasoned, so there she should find the most clues about Netta.

Katie dragged the rocker back to the kitchen with what seemed a dreadful scraping in the silence of the deserted house.

Katie John studied the kitchen, trying to imagine the freckled girl working in it: heavy old black cookstove, battered counter and the sink with the pump in it for water, shelves too high for easy reaching, the scarred wooden table on one wall, rocker in the corner by a window. Of course, the floorboards weren't broken then, and the kitchen wasn't so dirty and worn out. Still, what a dreary place for that merry-looking girl to come stepping lightly. This was a kitchen for a heavy-footed, middle-aged farm wife, whereas Netta, with the wide band over her hair, looked more as if she were setting out for bicycling. What a puzzle! A snub-nosed girl with speckled cheeks, a silk fan, and a farm wife's kitchen. How did they all connect?

The *Farmer's Almanac* was still on the shelf where Edwin had found it. Katie John sat in the rocker to look at the almanac. She leaned back, rocking with a steady creak.

Sometimes people wrote notes to themselves on calendars. Katie jumped up to look at the 1932 calendar hanging by the stove. No, if anything had been written on the dates, the writing had long since faded away. Well then, there was nothing left but the clippings.

There was no window over the sink; Netta must have put up the clippings to have something to look at as she washed dishes. They covered an area about three feet wide and two feet deep—Netta's "picture window," now yellowed and water-spotted. Katie John's heart beat faster as she climbed onto the counter and began reading the top row. There were faded newspaper articles on business opportunities in California and the wonderful California weather, and right below them a picture of shaggy camels. Katie gave up trying to read the clippings in any orderly fashion and looked them all over. There was a page of pictures identifying various kinds of owls, an article on the proper treatment for different kinds of poisoning, a picture of mountains, and a picture of a castle.

In the middle of the "window" was a magazine drawing of two boys on a raft floating on a river. There were other articles and pictures, but Katie was most interested in a homemade valentine and some children's drawings. Family things!

The valentine was a heart cut out of red paper. There was writing on it. With careful fingers,

Katie loosened the valentine from the wall. On the back was printed in capitals, "I LOVE YOU, MAMA. PATTY."

Netta had had a daughter! And Netta was the kind of mother who'd put up her little girl's first valentine and look at it forever and never take it down.

Now for the drawings. One was a crayon drawing. It showed the usual thing a child draws when he's first starting out: a square house with a pointed roof, a big yellow sun with lines for rays, and a tree covered with red dots for apples. The drawing was very faded, yet Katie could make out printing in one corner. It looked like "Wingter"— no, "Winston." Netta's son! The other drawing was on a sheet of lined notebook paper, and the work was quite good. It showed an eagle in flight. A name was signed in the corner: "Hal Calkins."

Calkins! The same name that was scratched on the doorframe. Katie's mind flashed, putting things together. The Calkins family had lived here, and no doubt Mr. Calkins had built this house for his bride Netta. A young farmer who could build, a young bride with freckles and a fan, then at least three children.

Well, she'd learned quite a bit about Netta this morning! For a minute Katie felt proud. And yet— and yet—she still hadn't found what she was looking for. She wasn't even sure she knew what she'd been looking for, except that—somehow she still didn't see how the freckled girl and the fan and the farmhouse kitchen could all be a part of the same person.

Oh, why do you make such a bother? Katie said to herself. You wanted to find out about the family like an archeologist studying, and you did. What difference does the girl make to you?

Nevertheless, the troubled, unanswered feeling remained.

She hooked the valentine back onto its wall-tack and walked out the back door toward the barn. Maybe she'd find some clue in the barn, though she doubted it.

Katie John stopped. A sound had come from beyond the barn. She wasn't sure what kind of sound except that it was one you didn't hear in deserted fields. She ran forward as softly as she could.

Behind the barn and off to one side toward the woods was a gully, and more rustling sounds came from there. She tiptoed toward the gully until she could look down into it, a spot where rain water had gradually worn the hill away.

And there was Edwin Jones. He was pulling apart the brush and matted grass in the gully. On a cleared spot of the ground by him were laid out an old black purse, stiff with rain and years, a broken pink doll, and other odds and ends such as a dented coffee pot and some toy wagon wheels.

Katie understood. Here in this gully the Calkins family had thrown away its trash. Edwin had found the place, under the years of brambles and mouse nests, and he was excavating it the way an

archeologist would. For a moment Katie watched him work, carefully, gently pulling apart weeds and scraping at something in the bank so as not to disturb the way anything else buried might lie.

Edwin looked up at her. She hadn't made a sound; yet Edwin had felt her presence somehow.

"What do you want?" Edwin's voice was abrupt, unfriendly. It seemed to say, "I'm busy, go away."

She felt a miserable twisting inside of her. There was Edwin, finding clues about the Calkins family. And she could have been so much help to him digging, carrying finds up to the house to keep them out of further weather. It could have been so much fun together.

When Katie didn't answer, Edwin shrugged and bent his head back to his work.

She turned and ran to the other side of the field, toward the place she'd left her bike. When she was safe down the bank into the creek bed of the glen, the tears came. Katie John sobbed, stumbling over the rocks.

There was something to be learned from Netta, Katie John could feel it, yet she put the thought aside for a while. Then came a clear, crisp November morning, a perfect Saturday for nutting. As Katie pedaled her bike out to Wildcat Glen, she told herself she was only going for the walnuts. But when she got there she knew why she'd been drawn there: she had to look at Netta's picture window again!

In the kitchen she stood before the sink and looked up at Netta's picture window. Nothing had disturbed the scenes of California, the pictures of different kinds of birds, the castle, and the river-raft scene in the middle of it all. Right in the middle—right in the center—something clicked into place. In matters of this sort you work from the center out.

So here was the clue to Netta's picture window! Work from the center out, and she'd know the order in which Netta had put the clippings. Instead of a faded, tattered jumble on the wall, Netta's picture window would reveal a running diary of what she'd cared about the most. She'd learn Netta's story yet!

With excitement Katie John began. Smack in the center, surely the first, was the picture of two boys on a raft floating down the river, a magazine drawing done in a bygone style. Still, it gave the feeling of lapping water and lazing on the sun-warmed boards of the raft.

"Oh, yes," Katie John breathed softly. What difference if Netta had been a girl in the days of long skirts and high blouses? She'd been a river kid, and she'd felt the call of the river the same as the boys. Maybe she'd even gone out on a raft once. And now that she was grown, she'd put up the picture in memory of river-rafting days. Dear Netta. Katie John hoped she'd gone rafting at least once before she had to put up her hair and be a lady.

Arranged around the river-raft drawing were the pictures of the castle, the shaggy camels, jagged snowy mountains. The young bride had dreamed of faraway places, Katie told herself. Also a couple of newspaper clippings. One was the poem about the delights of going barefoot. If she'd gone river-rafting and barefoot in those ladylike days, she must have been a tomboy, Katie thought. The other clipping was a recipe for bleaching freckles. Across it, "HA!" had been printed in heavy ink so many years ago. Katie smiled. Netta's freckles had bothered her, but she could laugh at herself when the recipe didn't work.

Widening out in more or less of a circle, Katie John found next the articles on baby care, the page of pictures identifying different kinds of owls, and then the family things. There were the child's drawing of a house, the homemade valentine, and Hal Calkins' drawing of an eagle. All these had been most important to Netta.

Katie John could see the farm wife coming through in the article of advice on when to plant vegetables according to the seasons and the time of the moon. But there were also clippings on how to trap animals of the woods without killing them and how to make guest-stations for wild animals. Had Netta done that with her children? Ah, yes, remember the wildcat—had they shivered about the wildcat too?

Then came a faded newspaper clipping about the hard times farmers were having during the Depression. Next to it was a recipe for making your own soap to save money. And finally, on the outside rim of the "picture window," colored magazine photos of California and the articles about business and farm opportunities in California.

So that's what had happened, why they'd left! Katie John had heard her parents speak of the Depression years in the early 1930's. People were poor then and farmers lost their farms because they had borrowed money on their land and then couldn't pay back the money, or because they couldn't get good enough prices for their crops to make a living. Maybe that had happened to the Calkins family. California must have spelled a wonderful new chance. And Netta and her husband had been brave enough to take it. In July, 1932, the last month showing on the calendar by the stove, the Calkins family had moved out, gone to California.

There was an awful lot of guesswork in figuring out all that, Katie John realized. A real archeologist probably would have needed lots more facts to go on. Some people might even say she'd just made it all up. But that was Netta's story as she understood it. She believed it.

And now that she knew Netta's story, what difference did it make? Why had she wanted so much to know about Netta? Why had she been drawn out here today?

Katie John sat down in the left-behind rocker at the other end of the room. Something was about to happen, she felt, and she'd like to be sitting down for it. Each hand took hold of the other in her lap, and she sat without rocking.

It mattered because this tomboy Netta had managed to grow up and still stay her own self. Don't get mixed up in words, Katie John cautioned herself. Now, if ever, she must think straight. Netta hadn't been one of those sweet little girls who did nothing but play dolls and tea party. This girl with the honest freckled face (but don't forget the sparkle in her eyes that said, "I've got a mind of my own") had her own special ways. Just like me, Katie thought. She'd had to come out of childhood into a ladylike world. Yet she'd handled it all right and stayed herself.

The fan. Did it mean Netta had gone along with the crowd for awhile, being a lady with her hair up? Katie John didn't believe that, else why had Netta kept the fan, treasured it? Maybe Netta had come to enjoy the womanliness that the fan stood for. Katie John wasn't sure what she herself meant by womanliness. Well, she'd find out about womanliness in time. Plenty of time . . . And the reason why Netta had left the fan behind? Now the question didn't bother Katie. It might be simply that Netta had forgotten it. She'd been so busy getting her family ready for the move, so eager for the new life ahead. The important thing was that a tomboy girl had handled growing up.

If she could do it, I can do it, too, Katie nearly shouted.

Too excited to sit longer, Katie John ran out the back door into the sunlight.

"Ah!" She breathed a great sigh of relief.

"Good-by, Netta, old pal," she said. "Thanks!"

She ran across the field, slid down the creek bank and found her bicycle. She'd forgotten to eat her lunch, so she ate the sandwich as she pedaled home. But the warm glow inside her didn't come from the food or the rays of the setting sun on her back.

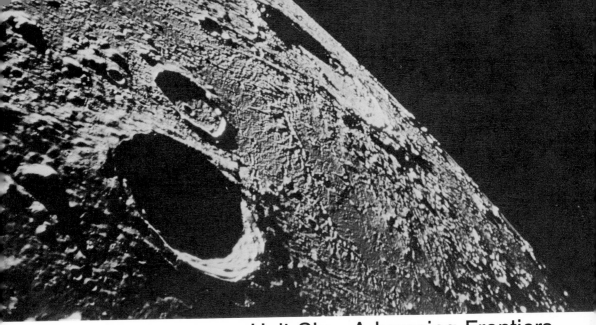

Unit Six   Advancing Frontiers

THE ELIXIR OF LONG LIFE

The flower blooms and soon withers away; a man is born to pass his few years on earth, and soon old age and death claim him—such is the unchangeable law of all life. My young friend, you remember the story of how, once upon a time, a man named Ponce de León sought in vain for the Fountain of Youth, said to be somewhere in Florida, that he might drink of its magic water and remain forever young.

Many of the old Chinese emperors also tried to discover the secret of eternal youth—they did not want to die. So they commanded the alchemists, men who worked in dark chambers with drugs and medicines, to distill the precious fluid that would give eternal youth: the Elixir of Long Life. These alchemists of old also spent their whole lifetime trying to find the so-called Philosopher's Stone which, they believed, could turn all metals into gold. But none succeeded in the great quest.

Emperor Han Wu-ti, upon the advice of the alchemists in his court, had a towering pillar built in his palace, on top of which was placed a big

bowl. This was to catch the precious dew-drops of the night—the drink of the fairies, which, it is claimed, when drunk by man gives him eternal youth.

One day some alchemists presented a flask of the precious elixir to Emperor Wu-ti. In his absence, an official of the court named Tung-fang Su stole the flask and swallowed the contents.

Emperor Wu-ti was exceedingly angered to find that his precious elixir had been stolen. He sentenced the man to die.

But Tung-fang Su knelt down and said to the emperor: "Your Majesty, true, I have stolen and drunk your Elixir of Long Life. If it is real, then you cannot harm me, for I shall live forever; but if it is not, then what harm have I done?"

Emperor Wu-ti was so stricken by the force of this logic that he broke into a smile and instantly pardoned the witty man.

Our word **elixir** was taken from *al-iksir,* a Medieval Arabic word derived from a Greek word for "the powder used in drying and healing wounds." In medieval times, an elixir was a chemical thought to have the power to change lead and iron into gold.

Sequence

If a cook doesn't use the right ingredients when baking a cake, or if she uses the right ingredients but mixes them in the wrong sequence, her cake will be a "flop."

A writer must put ideas together with the same care a cook would exercise in combining the ingredients in making a cake. Carefully constructed sentences are the writer's "ingredients." But the best ingredients will turn into a written flop if they are not combined in the proper sequence.

The sentences in the following description are out of sequence. Rewrite the description, putting the action in proper sequence. Begin with the sentence "The alarm jingled."

THE ALARM JINGLED. "Karen," a stern voice called, "you'll be late for school." The covers landed in a heap at the foot of the bed, and the search for the house slippers began. Once the alarm was shut off, the hand disappeared into the folds of the blankets and the room fell into silence. A rumpled head of hair emerged, after which a pair of squinty eyes became visible. A hand poked out from under the mountain of blankets and searched the nightstand for the clock.

HAPPY ACCIDENTS

Leo Baekeland increased the amounts of formaldehyde and carbolic acid in the beaker and turned the flame higher than usual.

During the months of experimentation he had noted that by varying the quantity of each chemical, by changing the intensity of the heat, and by stirring or not stirring, he could obtain mixtures with different properties. Although he could not determine beforehand what kind of mixture he would get, one thing was certain—he was on the right track. Eventually this process would result in a better varnish.

Suddenly the mixture began boiling violently, and hot particles were spewn all over the room. Baekeland and his assistant dived for cover. As they peered from their shelter, the mixture began to overflow the beaker, gradually stopped boiling, and started to harden.

Cautiously Baekeland approached the beaker, turned off the gas, and examined the hard mass that had formed. Whatever this mysterious substance was, it was not varnish! It was a stubborn gray mass. However, Baekeland realized that its very stubborness was what would make it valuable. Now he had to find a way to shape it.

Day after day Baekeland and his assistant tried to soften the irregular gray mass. But regardless of what they used, nothing had any effect on it— neither chemicals, intense heat, pressure, nor electrical current.

Months of unsuccessful experiments followed. Finally, in 1909, a method of molding the substance was discovered and the product was named "Bakelite." With this discovery began what is one of today's biggest industries—plastics.

Leo Baekeland and countless other scientists have set out in search of one thing and through an accident or unforeseen event have discovered something else—often more valuable than what they were seeking.

In 1754 an English writer by the name of Horace Walpole coined a word for such "happy accidents"—*serendipity*. It means "the ability to find unexpected things that are often more valuable or agreeable than the things sought after." The word comes from *Serendip*, the name of a country in the fifth-century fairy tale "The Three Princes of Serendip." In this tale, the three princes were always discovering unexpected things.

The history of scientific inquiry is filled with examples of serendipity and the frontiers of science have been advanced greatly because of it.

Charles Goodyear had spent years trying to find a means of processing rubber so that it would not turn into goo in the summer heat or become stiff and brittle in the winter cold. By 1839 he knew he was closer to solving the problem than he had ever been. He was getting fairly good results by adding sulphur to melted crude rubber. But something was still missing.

Then one evening when Charles was showing a bit of rubber to a friend, he accidentally dropped it onto a hot stove. Disgustedly, Charles dipped a second spoonful of rubber from the kettle and scraped the "ruined" bit of rubber from the stove with an iron poker. Suddenly Charles began to dance around the room like a man gone crazy, then dashed out of the house and thrust the piece of rubber into a snowbank to test it.

At last he had found the answer! This rubber, mixed with sulphur and *then* exposed to intense heat, was flexible in cold, yet firm in heat.

The accidental dropping of that bit of rubber led to the development of the process—vulcanization of rubber—which makes thousands of useful rubber products possible.

One day in the year 1895 an absent-minded professor, **Wilhelm von Roentgen** was working in a laboratory in Germany. When he left the lab, he forgot to disconnect the electric current to the vacuum tube he had been using in his study of cathode rays.

The professor, whose hobby was photography, had also left an unexposed photographic plate under a stack of books on a table in the same room. Later he used the plate to take a picture of some scenery. When he developed the picture, he was puzzled by a key-shaped shadow that appeared in the middle.

But how did it get in the middle of the picture? Professor Roentgen walked quickly back to his laboratory. He began to trace his actions, step by step, to find where he had kept the plate. Oh yes, it had been underneath that stack of books.

Continuing his scientific backtracking, the professor studied the outline of the key. Which of his keys could it be? Yes, it was exactly like the office key he had misplaced again. Now where was it this time? He then remembered that he had been using it as a bookmark during an experiment.

The professor picked up a book from the table and shook it. Out dropped the office key. Then von Roentgen remembered that the plate had been in the room when the cathode ray tube had been accidentally left burning.

So, through a series of seemingly unrelated accidents—and thanks to a very absent-minded professor—medical science obtained one of its most useful tools, X ray.

In the late 1800's a husband-and-wife team of researchers, **Marie and Pierre Curie,** made scientific history with the discovery of radium. This discovery changed many theories about the atom and the composition of matter. However, the Curies

were not satisfied. True, they had made a great discovery, but they realized that there was much more to be learned about this mysterious substance.

One day a friend and fellow scientist came into the Curies' laboratory and showed Pierre a burn on his abdomen. Radium, he told Pierre, had caused it. About a week before, he had put a piece of radium in his coat pocket and had forgotten about it for several hours. The burn had appeared a few days later, and although it looked as though it should be painful, it did not hurt at all.

Why did radium burn the skin? What would happen to skin which had been burned? Question piled upon question and the Curies had to find the answers. Further research led to the discovery that radium therefore could be used in treating diseases of the skin and body tissue, especially cancer.

The history of the world, as well as the history of scientific inquiry, is filled with such stories of "happy accidents."

Ponce de León was looking for the Fountain of Youth and discovered Florida.

Columbus set out in search of a new route to the Indies and discovered North America.

Even your own life is filled with examples of "serendipity."

1. How do you think Baekeland's training helped him realize that the mysterious substance in the beaker could prove valuable?

2. Why do you think Goodyear's discovery of vulcanization is an example of serendipity?

3. Did von Roentgen do a good "detective job" to discover what caused the key-shaped shadow in the middle of a picture? Why or why not?

4. Can you think of other "happy accidents" similar to the ones you have just read?

Vulcanization is a coined word made up of *Vulcan*, the name of the Roman god of fire, and the word elements *-ize*, "become," and *-ation*, "state of." Why is this a good word for the processing of rubber?

Marvels To Muse On

Reflect upon how substitutes
For metal, stone, and wood
Have changed the aspect of our world—
Restyled our lives for good.

Imagine what is yet to come—
The prospects are fantastic!
Someday they'll find the ultimate,
A substitute for plastic.

Grasping the Main Idea

Grasping the main idea is an important part of reading, especially when you are dealing with factual material. Studying demands that you summarize what you read. A good way to do this is to put the main idea of what you have read into one or two sentences.

Read the following selection, then select the best summary statement from the five which follow. Discuss your choice and give reasons for it.

Compared with the animals of his time, early man seemed ill-equipped for survival. He had no fur coat to protect him from heat and cold; no horns, hoofs, fangs, or tusks to use as weapons. Man could not run swiftly, yet he managed to survive while many of the beasts which pursued him became extinct.

Man had several advantages over animal. His ability to walk upright freed his hands for other tasks. His opposable thumbs enabled him to grasp objects. But his most valuable assets were his abilities to reason and to communicate ideas. Because he could think and reason, he could plan ways to clothe and shelter himself as well as develop tools and weapons. His ability to communicate ideas enabled him to share his discoveries.

1. Life was difficult for early man.
2. The cold caused early man to suffer.
3. His intelligence is the main reason why early man survived and improved his life.
4. Early man could not run very fast.
5. Early man had no horns, hoofs, fangs, or tusks to use as weapons.

Now read the following paragraphs. Think about the main idea and write a sentence to summarize it.

Our planet Earth, which we think of as being so huge, is really only a tiny part of our solar system. It is one of nine planets in orbit about our sun. Four of these planets—Mercury, Pluto, Mars, and Venus—are smaller than Earth; and four—Neptune, Uranus, Saturn, and Jupiter—are larger.

Earth is sixteen times larger than the smallest planet, Mercury. Jupiter, the largest planet, is one thousand three hundred times larger than Earth!

Our solar system is one small part of a huge galaxy called the Milky Way. The Milky Way, made up of about one hundred billion stars, is only one of countless galaxies which make up the Universe.

AUDUBON: WILDLIFE ARTIST

Bullfrogs grumbled about the bird songs that
filled the swamp air. The occasional booming
roar of an alligator rolled across the warm black
waters. John Audubon sat tired and dejected with
his thirteen-year-old companion, Joe Mason. Both
of them had struggled through waist-deep waters

and had yet to find any birds worth painting or sketching.

Suddenly, the air was split by a strange cry— *yank—yank—yank!*

"What was that, John?" asked a startled Joe.

"I don't know but I'm going to find out!" cried Audubon as he leaped to his feet and scrambled to collect his sketch pad and pencils. "The sound came from that cypress grove east of us!"

They plunged into the murky swamp water and struggled through the mud and great tangles of water lilies. The same cry, like the sound of a clarinet, *yank—yank—yank*, drew them deeper into the dark shade of the towering cypress swamp.

"Look!" cried Audubon. "At the top of that tree on your left!" He pointed to a flash of scarlet darting in and out of branches high above and asked, "Joe, do you think you can climb up and bring that bird out of its nest?"

"I sure can," answered Joe, for this was not the first time Mason had climbed a tree to capture an important bird for John Audubon's collection. Soon he was high overhead crawling among the branches into which the bird had disappeared.

"I've got 'im—I've got 'im!" Joe hollered. Though Joe was scratched and bleeding, he held the bird up for Audubon to admire.

"What a find, Joe! It's an ivory-billed woodpecker. Hold him carefully, now," cautioned Audubon as he began to examine the black and white markings on the woodpecker's body, and noted the brilliant scarlet crest. Mud, snakes, insects—all were forgotten in the excitement of the moment.

This John Audubon, standing waist deep in the waters of a Louisiana swamp, was very different from the Audubon who had arrived in America in 1803. Born in 1785, the son of a wealthy French sea captain, Audubon had come to America to manage the family estate at Mill Grove, Pennsylvania.

Because he was interested more in parties and wandering through the Pennsylvania woods than in business, John learned very little about how to run the estate. But he did improve on his skill as an artist. John was constantly observing and sketching the birds he encountered in neighboring woods.

It was during these early years in America that Audubon banded a pair of phoebes to see if the same pair would return to the nest in the spring. He tied silver wire around their legs and set them free. In the following spring, Audubon eagerly awaited the return of the birds. His patient observation of last year's nest was rewarded when the same two phoebes returned and began rebuilding their nest. This seems to have been the first banding

Courtesy Chicago Historical Society
(opposite page)

of birds in America, a practice widely used by conservationists today.

In 1807 Audubon attempted to become a businessman. Chasing around the woods after birds was not a very secure job in America. John went into partnership in a general store with Ferdinand Rozier, a former neighbor in France.

Both young men moved to Louisville, Kentucky, which was little more than a frontier trading post. It seemed that John was finally going to settle down. About that time he married Lucy Bakewell, whom he had known in Mill Grove.

But in every direction around Louisville lay the great American forest with its rich supply of animal life. The temptation was too great and soon Audubon was back to painting as many different kinds of birds as he could find.

Often, John would be gone for days following some new and interesting bird. He had learned how to live off the land from his own experiences and from his friendships with George Rogers Clark

Florida Jay

GARRULUS FLORIDANUS

Drawn from Nature

and Daniel Boone. These continued absences didn't seem to bother Lucy but they did bother his business partner. Rozier quarreled with Audubon and soon the partnership was dissolved.

John opened a new store in Henderson, Kentucky and for awhile was content to spend time in building the business. He continued to paint and to develop his ability to capture the natural coloring of the birds he found.

Lucy encouraged John in his painting and several people told him he should have his work published. Audubon didn't think seriously about painting for money until once again his business failed. This last failure in 1820 convinced John that he should turn to painting for his career.

This was a hard decision to make because it meant that John would have to leave Lucy and his two sons for an extended period of time. Lucy seemed to sense John's unborn greatness and insisted that he begin his travels to paint the "birds of America."

So it was that Audubon traveled down the Mississippi River in 1820 to begin his search for American birds. With only his painting supplies and his gun, Audubon set out on a trip that was to last until 1826. He lived for awhile in New Orleans and on various plantations in Louisiana and Mississippi. But he only stopped long enough to earn money to support himself while he continued to paint.

In 1822 he tried to have some bird paintings published in America. But he was not accepted by scientists and publishers in the East and had to return to the South to continue painting.

In 1826 John traveled to England in an attempt to have his paintings published. It was easy to find a publisher there. But Audubon also had to find people who would be willing to pay for the books before they were published.

Unknown and with few recommendations from America, Audubon had to convince people that his collection, *Birds of America*, would be an art collection worth having. Slowly the spark of genius in his work, and undoubtedly in his personality, began to fill the subscription book for his paintings. However, it was not until 1829 that enough subscribers could be counted on to make Audubon's publishing project a success.

This time success did not desert Audubon. Money from the sale of his *Birds of America* enabled John to write and publish a book about the birds he had painted. This book, called *Ornithological Biography*, was an immediate success. In 1843 John made his last expedition, a long-dreamed-of trip up the Missouri River. He painted the wildlife he observed and soon published an account of that trip.

Audubon's work still lives on. Even now, his original approach to the painting of birds captures one's imagination. The life-size paintings were the first of their kind. They opened the way for other naturalists to preserve something of the beauty in American wildlife for all the world to enjoy.

---

1. Would you have taken Joe Mason's place on the trip down the Mississippi River? Why or why not?

2. How do you think the skills of frontier hunters such as Daniel Boone helped Audubon collect birds to paint?

3. How do you think Lucy helped Audubon in his painting career?

4. How does the banding of birds help conservationists today?

5. In your own words, how would you describe John James Audubon to someone who didn't know anything about him?

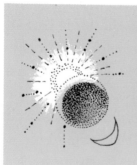

The Latin word *oriri* means "to rise," referring especially to the sun and the moon, and also "to begin." An English adaptation, **original,** more often refers to new ideas or things.

Summarizing a Selection

In "Happy Accidents" on page 385, the names of Ponce de León and Columbus are printed in boldface (heavy) type. From what you know of these two men, could you say that the sentence in which each name appears summarizes the reason why the man is remembered?

Now turn to page 378. Whose name appears in boldface on this page? What did this man contribute to science or technology?

Skim the rest of the selection and note the names in boldface type. Think about the contributions each of these persons has made to the advancement of the frontiers of science or technology. Write a sentence that summarizes the work of each.

Recall what you know about Babe Didrikson (page 23), Carl Akeley (page 92), Helen Keller (page 202), and Major Powell (page 246). Write a sentence summarizing the accomplishments of each of these persons.

If you cannot recall any facts about any of these persons, turn to the biographical sketch. A glance at the illustrations may be enough to refresh your memory. If not, reread the story quickly, then write your summary sentences.

TRACKS ON THE MOON

Since the dawn of his time, man has been wondering about the moon—the strange silver ball in the sky that governs the tides of the earth's oceans. Man has viewed the moon as a dead world of primitive rock, pock-marked by a continuous space rain of meteorites. The moon remained a subject of myth and beauty, a mystery in the sky until . . .

On July 16, 1969, at 9:32 A.M. (EDT) Apollo 11 blasted off from Cape Kennedy on its trip to the moon, a manned landing and return to earth.

The Apollo 11 had three parts: the command module (CM), the service module (SM), and the lunar module (LM).

The CM was shaped like a flattened cone with a bottom width of about 13 feet, stood 11 feet tall, and weighed about 13,000 pounds. Packed into its interior were the astronaut couches, food, space suits and helmets, toothbrushes, and sunglasses. The CM also contained instruments, radios, cameras, flight plans, and recovery parachutes.

The SM was also about 13 feet in diameter, but was 24 feet tall and weighed about 52,000 pounds. It housed electrical power supply equipment in a 22,000-pound thrust engine. The SM would drop away from the CM before the CM's re-entry into the earth's atmosphere.

The LM, code-named "Eagle," was about as high as a two-story house, weighed sixteen tons, and looked like a giant spider. It had gold and black markings to absorb and reflect the heat of the sun.

On the thrust of a rocket engine in its belly, the LM would begin the descent to the moon after its separation from "Columbia," the CM. Pilot Michael Collins would maintain the Columbia in

lunar orbit while awaiting the LM's return. The spindly, spidery-looking legs of the LM would support it on the lunar surface.

As the 69-inch probes beneath three of the bug's four footpads touched down, flashing a light on the instrument panel, Neil A. Armstrong, Commander of the LM, shut off the Apollo's engine. And the craft settled down with a jolt like a jet landing on a runway. Armstrong immediately radioed Mission Control: "THE EAGLE HAS LANDED."

July 20, 1969—on a patch of moon called *Tranquility Base*—on this day a new era began for man.

This tiny moon patch was inhabited for 21½ hours by Neil A. Armstrong, Commander of the Apollo 11, and his fellow explorer, Edwin E. Aldrin, Jr. Thus, the moon, once just an object of man's curiosity, became man's first temporary settlement in a new world.

Then, at 10:39 P.M. (EDT), as millions of earth men and women watched TV, Armstrong opened the LM hatch and squeezed through the opening. Slowly, he descended the nine-step ladder with equipment strapped to his shoulders.

Finally, at 10:56:20 P.M. (EDT), Neil Armstrong put his left foot on the moon and made history as he became the first man to ever step on anything that had not existed on or originated from the earth.

"THAT'S ONE SMALL STEP FOR A MAN: ONE GIANT LEAP FOR MANKIND," radioed Armstrong. Meanwhile, Aldrin was taking photographs from inside the spacecraft.

Armstrong surveyed his surroundings for a while and soon was joined by his companion, Aldrin. As scheduled, the astronauts then set up the first of three experiments. First, Aldrin removed a foot-long tube from the LM. This tube contained a roll of aluminum foil which contained a telescoped pole. Aldrin drove this pole into the lunar surface and suspended the foil from it, with the side marked "sun" toward the sun. Its function was to collect the particles of "solar wind" which blow constantly through space. Eventually these particles could be brought back and analyzed for information about how the sun and planets were formed.

After Armstrong and Aldrin had set up a U.S. flag on a staff pressed into the lunar surface, they received congratulations from President Nixon *via* Mission Control communications. Then Armstrong opened two specimen boxes into which he sealed a quantity of lunar rocks and soil to take back.

Meanwhile, Aldrin set up two devices on the moon's surface. First, he prepared a seismic detector to record moonquakes, meteorite impact, or volcanic eruption. Then he set up a laser-reflector, a device designed to make a much more precise measurement of earth-moon distances than had ever been possible before. This apparatus is similar to a mirror which has been carefully aimed at the earth.

After more than two hours on the lunar surface, the astronauts returned to the LM. Following a short, fitful rest, they prepared to leave the moon. The ascent into lunar orbit, where Collins awaited, began and continued in the same almost flawless style as the outbound trip to the moon.

With all three astronauts once again aboard, the CM left lunar orbit on schedule for the Thursday, July 24, splashdown in the Pacific. There the three encountered a strange combination of heroes' welcome and disease-carriers' quarantine. Sealed in a specially built isolation van, they remained in that environment until they arrived at the Lunar Receiving Laboratory in Houston.

Scores of scientists had gathered at the NASA Lunar Receiving Lab in Houston, anxiously awaiting the opening of the boxes of lunar rock samples brought back by Apollo 11's crew.

However, the scientists were not prepared for the surprises that turned up. Five of those unexpected discoveries were:

1. The surface rocks were extremely ancient—some of them about 3½ billion years old, comparable to the oldest exposed earth rocks ever found.
2. The erosion rate of the moon's surface rocks was much slower than scientists had estimated.
3. The moon's surface is covered with tiny glass bubbles and beads, comprising 10% or more of the lunar soil.
4. Surface rocks are pitted with many pockmarks and are coated with fused glass—the result of a continuous rain of cosmic matter.
5. Inside the rocks appear crystalline structures of clarity and beauty, which are very different from the cloudy quartz of earth granite.

Today, since scientists agree that it is unlikely there are living organisms on the moon, their interest is more in its origins, as a means of learning more about the earth.

The search goes on little by little. Man is extending his range of lunar exploration with ambitious plans for complete cities on the moon and orbiting lunar space stations able to support up to one hundred men.

Each new flight will result in new discoveries that will open whole new fields of scientific investigation. Future lunar flights will also pose new challenges for daring space adventurers who have now begun a fantastic program for roaming on foot over the distant planets.

---

1. Should man explore the moon and outer space? Why or why not?

2. What do you think Neil A. Armstrong meant when he said, "That's one small step for a man: one giant leap for mankind?"

3. What interesting facts did the scientists discover about the moon rocks brought back by the astronauts?

4. How did this exploration of the moon affect our earth's history?

How Strange It Is

In the sky
Soft clouds are blowing by.
Nothing more can I see
In the blue air over me.

Yet I know that planetoids and rocket cones,
Telstars studded with blue stones,
And many hundred bits of fins
And other man-made odds and ends
Are wheeling round me out in space
At a breathless astronautic pace.

How strange it is to know
That while I watch the soft clouds blow
So many things I cannot see
Are passing by right over me.

Making the News

HUGGINS BESTS CALLOWAY IN LEG-PULLING CONTEST! This headline recently appeared in the *Beaverdam Valley Times*. What story had the newspaper reporter written about?

When preparing headlines, newswriters have to follow some important rules. Their headlines must (1) be short and to the point; (2) give accurate information; and (3) arouse the reader's interest and curiosity. Did the writer of this headline follow these rules? Discuss this in class.

With what story would these headlines appear? TRAPPER "BEARLY" ESCAPES DEVIL'S JAWS. PROUD ROOSTER LANDS IN ROASTER. What might be some names for the papers in which each of these stories might appear?

If you were a reporter for the *Mount Olympus Express* in ancient Greece, you might be sent to cover the story "King Midas's Ears." Why would it be necessary to send several stories back to your editor? Your first story would probably be about the contest. What headline might it have? What other stories would follow? What other headlines?

Write headlines for the incidents in "Happy Accidents." Turn to the Table of Contents. Skim the titles and think about the stories. Pick at least three selections and write headlines for them.

HIS HEAD IN THE CLOUDS

I

It was a quiet morning at Long Island Spaceport. The *Queen Henrietta* was due in from Mars at 1303, with three hundred eighty aboard, and that was the big job of the day. At 1406 the liner *Madagascar* would blast off, carrying two hundred six.

Most of the passengers had arrived and were nervously smiling at each other as they paced up and down the waiting room. There hadn't been a major space disaster in a decade, but people still thought of space travel as risky.

There were a dozen private craft at the spaceport that morning, ranging from a heavy-duty freight boat to the slim two-man pleasure ship belonging to Nicholas Rocklin, the publishing tycoon. Rocklin's ship, *Cleopatra*, was in center position on the field ready for take-off later that same day, about 1352 said the arrival and departure blackboard.

The office of the spaceport's doctor, Claude Grosvenor, was quiet that morning too.

There had been one case. A young fueler had gashed his hand on a fuel line. Dr. Grosvenor had handled the job like the routine thing it was, cleaning, sterilizing, and sewing up the wound.

"Keep that hand out of action for a couple of days," Dr. Grosvenor said as he bound it. "Give it a chance to heal. And keep your mind on your work the next time you fuel a ship."

"Sure, Doc. Thanks a lot."

The fueler left and the doctor began to fill in the accident report on the fueler's record card:

Varangi, Simon F., age 20. Fueler, third class.

Grosvenor completed the card and refiled it. He sighed. One notation at the bottom of the card had hit him hard:

School: Federal Space Academy 12 Sep 2021. Discharged 14 Jan 2023, unsatisfactory reflexes.[1]

---

[1] In a spacecraft moving at speeds over 17,000 miles per hour, a space pilot must be able to act swiftly. The faster his reflexes, the faster he is able to react in emergency situations.

Grosvenor knew the pattern. A boy dreams of space for years, finally wins one of the few openings at the Academy, goes through his first few months or years—

And then the tests—the tests that tell him his vision is not good enough, his finger reflexes are a thousandth of a second too slow—any of the many tests that he must pass. That was the end. A space pilot had to be something of a superman, and not everyone fit the bill.

Oh, it was easy to get a spaceship into the air and pilot it around for awhile. But landing was a job for only a few. A spaceship out of control was the deadliest weapon known to man.

So people like Varangi hung on, at the spaceports. They took jobs as fuelers, hangarmen, as ticketsellers. Anything to stay near the big ships and watch them streak upward.

Even—Grosvenor thought moodily—*even as spaceport doctors:*

Grosvenor, Claude L. School: Federal Space Academy 14 Sep 1993. Discharged 11 Jan 1995, poor physical condition.

He had been here twenty-one years. Some men find second-best occupations, Grosvenor thought. But there was only one profession that mattered, and he had long since been cut off from that.

Grosvenor glanced up as the office door opened. He grinned at the tanned spaceman who stood there. "Hello, Lee. What brings you out here today?"

"Blasting off for Callisto this afternoon," Lee Ohmer said. "Old man Rocklin's taking a little vacation again."

"Ah, the pleasures of the idle rich," joked the doctor. "Enjoy it while you can, you've got four more years—." Grosvenor reddened; he realized that he had gone too far, to the point of hurting the pilot. Lee was twenty-six and when a spaceman reached thirty, he wrote an end to his career.

Which was worse, Grosvenor wondered: to go to space and have it all taken away from you at the age of thirty, or never to have gone at all?

Out loud he said, "I'm sorry, Lee. I guess I'm in a bad mood today. I didn't mean to joke about—about *that*."

"Don't worry about it, Doc. I'm not offended. I know what's griping you—and believe me, I feel for you. After all, I've *been* up there!"

Grosvenor had his answer. Just a taste of the sky's blackness, just a few moments above the clouds—that was worth a lifetime of grubby doctoring on the ground.

He turned away and stared out the window—the big picture window they had given him, so he could watch the graceful ships as they came and went.

"You've got to hand it to that Rocklin," Grosvenor said, his eyes on the sleek lines of the *Cleopatra*. "That ship of his must be the loveliest private job in the world."

"You're not kidding. And it's the smoothest, gentlest ship to pilot you could imagine. Why—"

"Must be something wrong with my eyes," declared Grosvenor.

"Huh?"

The doctor blinked several times. "I must be seeing things. It seems like your jets are firing; but that's impossible, isn't it?"

Ohmer chuckled and moved to the window. A quiet strangling sound rumbled up from his throat. "Do you see what I see?" he asked.

Grosvenor nodded.

The *Cleopatra* was twenty feet off the ground, standing on a tail of fire so bright it hurt the eyes. It wobbled for a second or two, then began to rise. Soon it arched through the atmosphere and was out of sight.

It couldn't have happened. But it had.

A few seconds later the wail of the emergency alarm siren began to shrill through the spaceport.

For Peter Michael Willer, who was fourteen, the day had begun in an ordinary fashion. The alarm had been set for 7:45 A.M., but Pete woke at seven. There were more important things to do than sleeping.

He glanced up at the books on his shelf—the brightly colored volumes labeled *How to Pilot Space Ships* and *Astrogation Made Easy.*[2] He knew every word of them by heart. He took them down, fondled their tattered pages, put them back.

He dressed slowly, tiptoed through the silent house, opened the front door. It was a bright, clear morning, and in the distance he saw the beacon tower of the Long Island Spaceport.

[2] Astrogation used to be a term you might find only in science fiction. Today, astronauts use astrogation to guide their space ships through the vast emptiness of outer space.

The mail had arrived. Peter snatched it up and shuffled through it.

Bills. Letters from his father, working on a top-secret space project. A comic book his silly sister subscribed to.

Ah! Here it is. He felt his heart begin to pound as he came across the official-looking white envelope:

Mr. P. M. Willer, Jr.

43 Red Maple Drive North

Levittown, Long Island

The return address was even more exciting:

Federal Academy of Astrogation

Admissions Office

Washington, D. C. 20006

Letting the other letters drop to the ground, Pete ripped it open and read it:

13 May 2023

Mr. P. M. Willer, Jr.
43 Red Maple Dr. N.
Levittown, Long Island
My dear Mr. Willer:

Thank you for your letter of 6 May. We are in receipt of your application for admission to the Academy, and have considered it most carefully.

On the basis of the information you give, I can safely say that you have the necessary enthusiasm and willingness to learn that marks a successful Academy candidate. However, you fail to toe the mark in one respect. Minimum age for admission to Academy is 18, and this cannot be waived in any case whatsoever.

Therefore, may I suggest that you contact us again in four years, when you will be eligible for admission? I'm sure there'll be room for someone of your potentiality in the Class of 2031, and I'll be looking forward to hearing from you again when you've completed your high school courses four years hence.

With all good wishes,
Col. Walter D. Thompson, USSC
Director of Admissions

Peter stared at the letter bitterly. *They turned me down.* He had never expected that. Hadn't he studied spaceflight for half of his life? Didn't he know the basic manuals backward and forward? They had no right to turn him down.

They had been very polite about it. Go away, little boy; come back in four years. *Four years!* He would be eighteen then. There would only be twelve years of space for him after that—and then he would be grounded, the way his father had been. And then he could only look up at the stars wistfully, remembering—

Peter clenched and unclenched his fists. Ahead of him, the shining beacon of Long Island Spaceport seemed to beckon to him.

"Pete!" his mother called. "Hurry up or you'll be late for school."

He turned and went into the house for breakfast.

Pete ate listlessly. You weren't supposed to eat for four hours before a spaceflight. Well, that was only until eleven or twelve o'clock.

"Have a good day at school, Peter," his mother called as he left the house.

"What? Oh—yeah. Sure, Mom. See you at three."

His closed briefcase was heavy with school books and the added weight of *Astrogation Made Easy* and *How to Pilot Space Ships.* If his mother saw them, she might wonder why he was taking them to school today.

I'll show them, he thought. *I'm not going to wait any four years.*

He reached the corner, and when he was out of his mother's line of sight, doubled back down a side street. Minutes later, he was aboard the bus heading toward Long Island Spaceport.

Tension began to gather around him. As he entered the bus, it seemed the bus driver was about to say, "You ought to be in school now. But I know why you're going to the spaceport. You're going to steal a ride in a spaceship!" The other passengers seemed to know just what Peter was thinking.

The trip from Levittown to the spaceport was longer than he remembered; it was nearly 0900 when he arrived. The bus let him off at the big gate.

The gray-uniformed guard looked through Pete's briefcase. "*Astrogation Made Easy,* huh? I guess that stuff is harmless enough. You got your eye on the academy?" he asked.

Pete nodded. "I put my application in already. They said I was too young."

The guard laughed, "Just a little," he said. But you'll have your chance in a few years. Good luck, too. I almost made it myself."

"You almost—" Pete stopped. "Oh, I see. I'm sorry."

The guard's smile faded. "It doesn't bother me much. But you'd better get moving. I'm not supposed to be talking on duty."

Peter went on in. The spaceport loomed up all around him—administration buildings here and there, and the big beacon tower, and fuel hangers. And out there was the vast landing field.

He saw the towering bulk of the *Madagascar*, the giant liner due to depart this afternoon. He saw the other smaller ships.

And he saw the slender *Cleopatra*, standing alone in the center of the field. His pulse rate jumped. This was the one for him!

II

It took nearly two hours for Peter to find out
what he wanted to know from an idle fueler.

"That's the *Cleopatra*, boy. Supposed to leave
about 1352. Lee Ohmer is the pilot—should be
around here somewhere—no, he's up in Doc's office

—Oh, yeah, it's fueled and ready to go."

The *Cleopatra* looked all alone, out there. It was fueled up and ready to go. Maybe they wouldn't notice one small boy sneaking around the back way—

They didn't. He arrived at the *Cleopatra* somewhat out of breath but totally unnoticed. The catwalk of the small vessel had been run out and the airlock was wide open.[3]

Quickly Peter began to climb. He expected them to start yelling any minute, but so far he hadn't been seen. People just didn't expect small boys to steal spaceships.

He reached the open airlock and climbed in. For a moment his mind went blank—then he closed his eyes and let the words of the manuals come flooding into the front of his mind, washing away the fear.

He was inside a spaceship. He knew exactly what to do.

He grabbed the red lever inside the airlock and yanked down on it, hard. The outer door slid shut with a soft hissing noise, and sealed. They wouldn't be able to get him out in time now.

---

[3] If a crewman must leave a spacecraft while in outer space, he leaves through an airlock, a compartment that can be sealed to prevent air from escaping from inside the space ship.

The inner lock opened; he stepped through hurriedly, and it clanged shut again.

Excitedly now he made his way to the fore control cabin, edging up the narrow companionway. He entered.

It was wonderful. There were the great windows from which he would be able to see the twinkling stars and the pockmarked face of the moon in a few minutes. Over the control panel was the ship-to-earth telescreen.

He swung himself into the pilot's seat. He was big for his age, but there was still plenty of room. He drew his instruction manuals out of the briefcase and spread them out within reach in case he needed them.

Then he proceeded to set the *Cleopatra* up for blastoff. He planned to circle the moon and return. *That* ought to prove to the Academy that he belonged there!

Pete glanced out the window to make sure none of the field workers was within range of the jets. He saw a few fuelers in the distance pointing at the *Cleopatra*, but they were safely out of range.

Calmly, he radioed Central Control and said, "This is Lieutenant Peter Michael Willer, aboard the *Cleopatra*. I'm blasting off for Luna now. Time exactly 1122—blasting off!" He jammed his forefinger down on the blasting key. Then he felt the jets throb beneath him—and a moment later the *Cleopatra* sprang away from the Earth's surface.

From the window of Doc Grosvenor's office, Lee Ohmer watched his ship taking off. His face was pale, unbelieving. "It's crazy. You can't just steal a ship. Rocklin will kill me!" he moaned.

Over the siren's wail came the boom of the public address system: *"Lieutenant Lee Ohmer, please report to Central Control at once. Lieutenant Lee Ohmer report to Central Control at once."*

The doctor and Ohmer arrived at Central Control on a dead run. Major General Mahoney, the Spaceport Commander, was pacing up and down the office.

"Ohmer? What's going on here? Your ship just made an unauthorized—"

"I know. I saw it take off. What kind of supervision does this place have, anyway? How did it happen?"

Mahoney shrugged. "We got a message just before the *Cleopatra* left. A Lieutenant Peter Michael Willer said he was blasting off, and he did."

It was like floating, Peter thought. Jets cut off, the ship sliced like a needle through the eternal blackness. There was no sense of motion; he seemed frozen in time and space.

But there was earth, a dwindling green sphere, the Americas visible in the classic view. And over there—that pockmarked globe growing larger was the Moon! The moon was cold and white and dead, a fishbelly color against a black velvet backdrop.

Everything was going perfectly. *Who said I can't pilot a spaceship!* he thought. *Here I am—making the Luna run solo!*

Suddenly the telescreen before him brightened. The face of a burly man in Space Corps uniform appeared. He looked angry. Peter grinned at him.

"Are *you* Lieutenant Willer?" the officer thundered. "Why—you're just a boy."

"I'm Pete Willer. Who are you, Major-General?"

"Mahoney. Base Commander. How did you get up there?"

"In a spaceship, Major-General Mahoney. It was easy!" Peter pointed to the manuals open on the control panel. "I've studied. I know how to run a spaceship. I'm good enough to get into the Academy."

"Why, you little delinquent! How—" The Major-General sputtered awkardly for a moment. "Bring that ship down instantly! That's an order!"

"Sorry, sir. I'm making a Luna run. I'll bring the ship down as soon as I've circled the moon. It won't take long." Peter smiled cheerfully. "Be seeing you soon, sir."

In Central Control, Lee Ohmer couldn't resist chuckling as he heard the conversation.

Mahoney, who had broken contact with the spaceship, regarded Ohmer coldly. "This is a very serious matter, Lieutenant. We'll have to bring that boy down on automatic. We can't trust him to land a ship by himself."

"But he seems to know—"

"*Seems* isn't good enough. A spaceship crashing into earth at full velocity could destroy a city. We'll have to immobilize his controls by remote wave and bring the ship back ourselves."

Ohmer shrugged. "If you think so, sir. But let him go around the moon first. As long as he got as far as he did, he deserves to see the other side."

The danger of an out-of-control spaceship was so great that ships were designed to be controlled from the ground.

This was done with the *Cleopatra*. Lee Ohmer manned the controls at Long Island Spaceport, after Peter had completed his round-the-Moon circuit and had started the return journey. Ohmer waited until the ship was well on its way toward Earth, then threw the switch freezing the ship's controls and cut in himself.[4]

There was an angry protest from Peter. "I can handle it! I know how to handle a landing orbit! I can—"

"Sorry," Ohmer said. "Can't risk it."

He guided the ship into proper positioning, shoe-horning it down toward Earth. As it swung into place and approached ground, Ohmer said, "Better strap down hard, son. It's going to be a lousy landing."

Ohmer flicked sweat off his brow and glanced over his shoulder at Grosvenor, who was tensely standing by. "Get the field cleared. And Doc, have an ambulance ready. I'm a microsecond off, and *Cleopatra's* going to come down with a bump."

"Okay." Grosvenor said.

"The kid could have done as well as this," said Ohmer as he hunched over the controls.

---

[4] Remote control systems use radios and other electronic equipment to control distant equipment. Computers are often an important part of a remote control system.

Moments later the *Cleopatra* appeared. It hung over the field for an instant, then dropped. The tail assembly crumpled; Ohmer winced. It had been a lousy landing, all right.

Lee arrived at the scene moments after Grosvenor. The doctor turned to Lee and said, "Come inside with me. I don't know my way around these ships."

Pete was still in the control cabin of the damaged ship, eyes closed, face very pale.

Grosvenor bent over him. After an anxious moment Ohmer said, "Doc, is he—"

"He's alive, if that's what you mean. Broken ribs, internal bleeding. He's in bad shape, but he ought to pull through."

"It was a lousy landing," Ohmer repeated. "A lousy landing. But the kid would have killed himself. No one can land a ship on the first try."

The boy stirred. From outside the angry voice of Mahoney bellowed, "Is that delinquent in there? I want to see him! We'll press charges! We'll—"

Ohmer walked to the lip of the ruptured ship. He looked out and said, "Shut up. The kid's hurt."

"He's waking up," Grosvenor said. The doctor shook his head sadly. "The poor kid. He'll never get into the Academy now—not the way he's banged up. He'll never pass the physical."

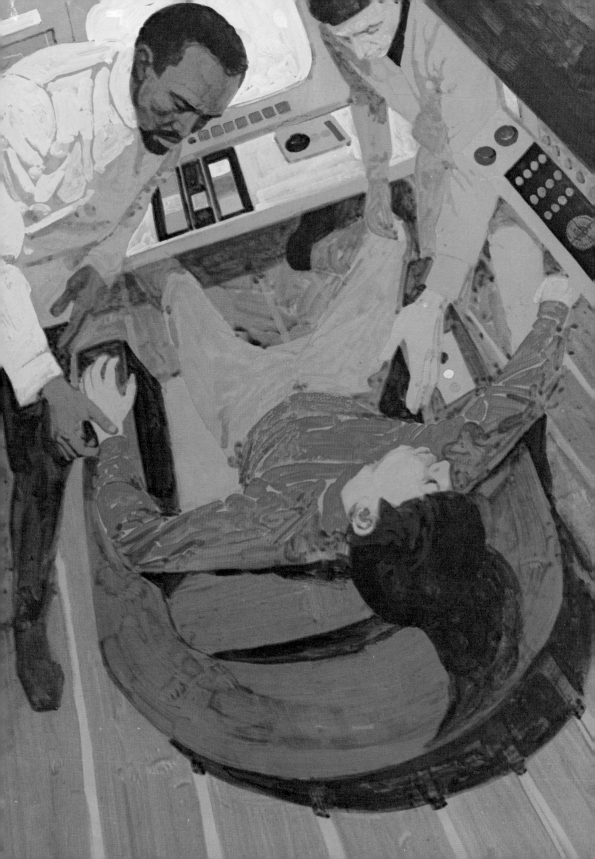

But, the doctor was thinking. *At least he got there once. He saw the backside of the Moon. I never even got there.*

The boy opened one eye, then another.

"Take it easy," Grosvenor said. "I'm the space-port doctor. You'll be all right. Just hold still."

The boy grinned weakly. "How'd I do, Doc? Did I do all right?"

Grosvenor nodded. "You did just fine, son. Just fine."

 The ancients believed that the stars influenced their lives. A **disaster** meant the "stars" were "against" them. *Disaster* was formed from a borrowed Greek word *astron* meaning "star." This last form may be seen in *astronaut*.

GLOSSARY

Pronunciation Key

The pronunciation key will help you to understand what the diacritical marks mean in the Glossary of *Coming To Crossroads*.

The principal, or heavy, accent is indicated by the mark ′ after a syllable. In some words another syllable is also accented, but not so heavily. Such a syllable has the mark ′ after it—called a secondary accent.

Many foreign languages are spoken with some sounds which do not occur in English. A symbol for such a sound is given at the end of this pronunciation key.

a as in hat	o as in hot	th as in thin
ā as in āge	ō as in ōpen	ᴛH as in then
ã as in cãre	ô as in ôrder	
ä as in fäther		zh as in measure
	oi as in oil	
e as in let	ou as in house	ə represents:
ē as in ēqual		a in about
ėr as in tėrm	u as in cup	e in taken
	ů as in fůll	i in April
i as in it	ü as in rüle	o in lemon
ï as in ïce	ū as in ūse	u in circus

French N: Do not pronounce the N. Its purpose is to show that the vowel before it is spoken with the nasal passage open so that the breath passes through both the nose and the mouth.

ç: This c with a cedilla (ç) is pronounced s.

The pronunciation system and key is taken from the Thorndike-Barnhart Dictionary Program. Copyright © 1968 by Scott, Foresman and Company.

A. General Glossary

a

-able (*suffix*), that which can be ___ed; deserving to be ___ed.

a brupt (ə brupt'), sudden; unexpected.

ab so lute (ab' sə lüt), complete; whole.

a cad e my (ə kad'ə mē), a school that trains students in a specific field or subject.

ac com mo date (ə kom'ə dāt), to provide lodging.

ac com pa ny (ə kum'pə nē), to go along with.

ac com plish (ə kom'plish), to complete successfully.

ac count (ə kount'), to explain.

ac cu mu late (ə kū'myə lāt), to collect; to pile up little by little.

ac cus tom (ə kus'təm), to get used to.

ac id (as'id), a chemical with a sharp, sour taste.

ac quaint (ə kwānt'), to come to know personally.

ac quire (ə kwïr'), to get as one's own by effort.

ac ro bat ics (ak'rə bat'iks), the performance of one skilled at tumbling or other stunts.

ad- (*prefix*), to; toward.

ad ept (ə dept'), skillful; expert.

a gent (ā'jənt), a cause or power that produces an effect; one who performs a certain act.

ag ri cul ture (ag'rə kul'chər), the raising of crops and livestock; farming.

aisle (īl), any long, narrow passageway between rows of seats.

-al (*suffix*), like; pertaining to.

al ter na tive (ôl ter'nə tiv), offering a choice between two or more items.

-an (*suffix*), of; having to do with.

an a lyze (an'ə līz), to examine carefully.

-ance (*suffix*), the act of.

An des (an'dēz), mountains near the western coast of South America.

An nap o lis (ə nap'l is), the capital of Maryland.

-ant (*suffix*), one that.

anti- (*prefix*), preventing.

anx ious (angk'shəs), worried; eagerly wishing.

ap pa ra tus (ap'ə rā'təs), a device or machine for a certain use.

ap par ent (ə par'ənt), plain to see; seeming.

ap pro pri ate (ə prō'prē it), suitable; proper.

A ra bi a (ə rā'bē ə), a large peninsula in southwest Asia.

ar che ol o gy (är'kē ol'ə jē), the scientific study of people, customs, and life in ancient times.

ar thri tis (är thrī'tis), a disease which causes the joints to swell and ache.

-ary (*suffix*), a person or thing that has, goes, does, etc.

as pect (as'pekt), appearance; side of a subject.

as sem bly (ə sem'blē), a meeting.

as sure (ə shür'), to make certain; tell positively.

as tro ga tion (as'trə gā'shən), the science of navigating a spacecraft.

-ate (*suffix*), having.

-ation (*suffix*), the act of being; the state of being.

at mos phere (at'məs fir), the layer of air surrounding the earth.

---

hat, āge, cãre, fäther; let, ēqual, tėrm; it, īce; hot, ōpen, ôrder; oil; house; cup, fùll, rüle, ūse; th, thin; ŦH, then; zh, measure; ə represents *a* in about, *e* in taken, *i* in April, *o* in lemon, *u* in circus.

at om (at′əm), in chemistry, the smallest unit of an element.

au di ence (ô′dē əns), people gathered to hear or see something; interview.

au thor i ty (ə thôr′ə tē), the power to enforce control over something or someone.

awk ward (ôk′wərd), clumsy.

b

bac te ri a (bak tir′ē ə), microscopic, single-celled organisms.

bam boo (bam bü′), a treelike tropical grass with hollow, jointed stems which are often used for making fishing poles, furniture, etc.

B.C., the initials which stand for "Before Christ"; used to designate the number of years *before* the birth of Christ in indicating dates.

beak er (bēk′ər), a thin glass, handleless cup with a small lip for pouring, used in laboratories.

blood cur dling (blud′kėr′dling), horrible.

boul der (bōl′dər), a large rock.

Brit ish Isles (brit′ish īlz), Great Britain, Ireland, and other nearby islands.

bron to sau rus (bron′tə sô′rəs), the largest member of the dinosaur family.

c

can cer (kan′sər), a very harmful growth in the body which tends to destroy healthy tissue.

car a van (kar′ə van), a group of traders, pilgrims, or tourists traveling on a long journey.

car bol ic ac id (kär bol′ik), a poisonous white liquid chemical.

cat a pult (kat′ə pult), to throw forcefully.

cath ode rays (kath′ōd), the invisible electrons that move at high speed (usually in a straight line) within a vacuum tube. They produce X rays.

cau li flower (kô′lə flou′ər), a type of cabbage with a white head of thickly-clustered flowers.

cau tious (kô′shəs), taking no chances.

cen taur (sen′tôr), a legendary Greek monster.

cer e mo ny (ser′ə mō′nē), very polite conduct; a set of acts to be done on special occasions.

chal lenge (chal′ənj), demand a duel; test of strength or courage.

chant (chant), to sing a short, simple song.

chris tie (kris′tē), a high-speed turn used in skiing.

clas si cal (klas′ə kl), based on the literature and art of ancient Greece and Rome.

cock a trice (kok′ə tris), a legendary beast which Europeans of the Middle Ages believed to exist.

com- (*prefix*), with; together.

com merce (kom′ərs), the buying and selling of goods; trading.

com mis sion (kə mish′ən), in working order.

com mis sion er (kə mish′ən ər), an official in charge.

com mo tion (kə mō′shən), a disturbance.

com mu ni ca tion (kə mū′nə kā′shən), the giving or receiving of information by talking or writing.

com pan ion way (kəm pan′yən wā′), the staircase that leads from the deck of a ship to the area below.

com part ment (kəm pärt′mənt), a separate part or section.

com pete (kəm pēt′), to take part in a contest.

com pos ite (kəm poz′it), made up of various parts.

com po si tion (kom′pə zish′ən), the make-up of anything; a short essay written as a school exercise.

com pre hend (kom′pri hend′), to understand the meaning of.

con- (*prefix*), a form of **com-**.

con cen trate (kon′sn trāt), to pay close attention.

con fi dent (kon′fə dənt), certain; sure of oneself.

con found (kon found′), to jumble; confuse.

con fuse (kən fūz′), to mix up.

con grat u late (kən grach′ə lāt), praise for something accomplished successfully and well.

con se quent (kon′sə kwent), following as a result.

con spic u ous (kən spik′yu̇ əs), easily seen.

con stel la tion (kon′stə lā′shən), a group of stars.

con tam i nate (kən tam′ə nāt), to make impure; pollute.

con tempt (kən tempt′), scorn; disobedience or open disrespect; disgrace.

con tour (kon′tu̇r), the outline of a figure.

cop per (kop′ər), a reddish-brown metal; a thing made of copper.

co qui (kō kē′), a tree frog.

cos met ic (koz met′ik), a preparation for making such things as the hair and skin more beautiful.

cos mic (koz′mik), relating to the whole universe.

coun cil (koun′sl), a group of people called together to give advice or settle questions.

coun te nance (koun′tə nəns), the expression of the face.

coun ter feit (koun′tər fit), a copy of something made to fool others.

court (kôrt), a place marked off for a game; a place for administering justice; those who administer justice.

cour te ous (kėr′tē əs), thoughtful of others; polite.

crest (krest), a bunch of feathers on the head of a bird; top of a hill; decoration on the top of a coat of arms.

cul ti vate (kul′tə vāt), to prepare and use land to grow crops; improve.

cur (kėr), a worthless dog.

cut lass (kut′ləs), a short, thick, curved sword.

d

de- (*prefix*), down.

de fi ant (di fī′ənt), bold.

del e gate (del′ə gāt), a person given the authority to act and speak for others; representative.

de lin quent (di ling′kwənt), a person who continually fails to obey the laws.

de pres sion (di presh′ən), bad times; often refers to "Great Depression" of the 1930's.

de spair (di spãr′), a loss of hope.

des per ate (des′pər it), frantic because of unhappiness and anxiety.

des ti na tion (des′tə nā′ shən), the place to which a person or thing is going.

di a logue (di′ə lôg), a conversation.

---

hat, āge, cãre, fäther; let, ēqual, tėrm; it, ῐce; hot, ōpen, ôrder; oil; house; cup, fu̇ll, rüle, ūse; th, thin; ᴛʜ, then; zh, measure; ə represents *a* in about, *e* in taken, *i* in April, *o* in lemon, *u* in circus.

di am e ter (dī am′ə tər), a line passing through the center of a circle with its end points on the circle.

dig ni fy (dig′nə fī), to make noble.

dip lo mat (dip′lə mat), a person who lives and works in a foreign country as a representative of his own nation.

dis- (*prefix*), not; loss; the opposite of.

dis crim i nate (dis krim′ənāt), to make a difference in favor of or against one person or thing.

dis cus (dis′kəs), a circular metal plate used in athletic games as a test of skill and strength in throwing.

dis mal (diz′ml), dark; gloomy; sad.

dis perse (dis pėrs′), to scatter in different directions.

dis rupt (dis rupt′), to disturb.

dis suade (di swād′), to persuade not to do something.

dis tinct (dis tingkt′), different from others; special.

dis tin guish (dis ting′gwish), to tell apart; make famous.

dis trib ute (dis trib′ūt), to give out in shares.

di vi sion (də vizh′ən), a part or section of a larger group.

-dom (*suffix*), the condition of being.

dra mat ic (drə mat′ik), full of action; exciting.

dun geon (dun′jən), a dark, underground prison room.

e

e clipse (i klips′), the darkening of the sun or moon when some other heavenly body moves so as to partly or wholly cut off its light.

ec sta sy (ek′stə sē), a state of great happiness.

ee rie (ir′ē), strange; causing fear.

e lab o rate (i lab′ə rit), very detailed; carefully planned.

el i gi ble (el′ə jə bl), qualified; worthy to be chosen.

e lix ir (i lik′sər), the substance supposed to have the power to lengthen life.

em bar rass (em bar′əs), to cause to feel mixed up and self-conscious.

em brace (em brās′), to hug.

e merge (i mėrj′), to come out.

e mer gen cy (i mėr′jən sē), something which must be taken care of immediately.

em pha sis (em′fə sis), stress; importance.

en- (*prefix*), make; in; into.

-en (*suffix*), to cause to be; cause to have; made of.

-ence (*suffix*), the condition of being.

en coun ter (en koun′tər), to meet unexpectedly; an unexpected meeting.

-ent (*suffix*), one that.

en vi ron ment (en vī′rən mənt), the conditions and influences that affect the growth and development of living things.

-er (*suffix*), a person or thing that; one who is in.

-ern (*suffix*), of; toward.

-ese (*suffix*), of or having to do with.

es tab lish (es tab′lish), to set up permanently.

es tab lish ment (es tab′lish-mənt), a business set up permanently.

e ter nal (i tėr′nl), lasting forever; without beginning or end.

-eth (*suffix*), form of **-th.**

e ven tu al (i ven′chù əl), final.

ex- (*prefix*), out; from.

ex cel (ek sel′), to be outstanding.

ex cep tion al (ek sep′shən l), above average; superior; out of the ordinary.

ex cur sion (eks kėr′zhən), a short trip usually for pleasure.

ex haust (eg zôst′), to use up; tire.

ex pe di tion (eks′pə dish′ən), a journey for some special purpose; group making such a journey.

ex pe ri ence (eks pir′ē əns), the knowledge gained by doing things.

ex per i ment (eks per′ə ment), to make tests.

ex pose (eks pōz′), to allow light to reach and act on a photographic film; uncover.

ex pres sion (eks presh′ən), a look that shows feeling.

ex tinct (eks tingkt′), no longer existing.

f

fan tas tic (fan tas′tik), unbelievable.

fas ci nate (fas′n āt), to interest.

fee ble (fē′bl), weak.

fe roc i ty (fə ros′ə tē), fierceness.

fidg et (fij′it), to be uneasy.

fig ur a tive language (fig′yər ə-tiv), a style of writing in which a writer uses comparison to help you understand his description of a specific thing.

fi nance (fə nans′), money matters.

flag on (flag′ən), a large bottle.

flex (fleks), bend.

for age (fôr′ij), to hunt or search about.

fore- (*prefix*), before; in front of.

for eign (fôr′ ən), outside one's own country.

form al de hyde (fôr mal′də hĭd), a colorless gas with an unpleasant odor.

fos sil (fos′l), the hardened remains of a plant or animal of a former age.

foun dry (foun′drē), the place where metal is melted by heat and then shaped.

fra grance (frā′grəns), a pleasing smell.

fran tic (fran′tik), greatly excited; wild with pain or fear.

fre quent (frē′kwənt), often; near together.

frit ter (frit′ər), a small batter cake, fried in fat.

froth (frôth), foam.

-ful (*suffix*), full of; having.

fum ble (fum′bl), to handle clumsily; to drop.

fur tive (fėr′tiv), secret; done slyly.

-fy (*suffix*), make.

g

gal ley (gal′ē), a long, narrow ship of former times having oars and sails.

gam bol (gam′bl), to jump or skip playfully.

gaunt (gônt), extremely thin and bony.

gen er a tion (jen′ər ā′shən), all the people born about the same time; about 30 years.

ge nie (jē′nē), a mythological being having magical powers.

gen ius (jēn′yəs), very great mental ability.

Gen ius (jēn′yəs), a god which the Romans believed protected a person.

---

hat, āge, cãre, fäther; let, ēqual, tėrm; it, ĭce; hot, ōpen, ôrder; oil; house; cup, fùll, rüle, ūse; th, thin; ŦH, then; zh, measure; ə represents *a* in about, *e* in taken, *i* in April, *o* in lemon, *u* in circus.

ge ol o gy (jē ol′ə jē), the science that deals with the layers of the earth's crust.

ges tic u late (jes tik′yə lāt), to make gestures.

ges ture (jes′chər), a movement of the hands, head, etc., to express an idea or feeling.

gib bon (gib′ən), a member of the ape family.

glen (glen), a small valley.

glum (glum), very sad and silent.

gnome (nōm), a make-believe dwarf who is supposed to live underground.

gran ite (gran′it), a hard rock.

-graph (*word element*), to write.

greed (grēd), wanting more than one's share.

grif fin (grif′ən), a mythical animal, part eagle and part lion. Also, *gryphon*.

guar an tee (gar′ən tē′), a promise that goods offered for sale are of good quality.

Gulf of Mex i co (mek′sə kō), a large bay between Florida and Mexico.

Gulf Stream, a warm ocean current that flows from the Gulf of Mexico northward through the Atlantic Ocean.

gy rate (jī′rāt), to move in a circle; whirl; spin.

h

haugh ty (hô′tē), proud of oneself and scornful of others.

Hei del berg (hī′dl bėrg), a German city in which a famous university is located.

hence forth (hens′fôrth′), from now on.

ho mog e nize (hə moj′ə nīz), to make alike.

hon ey suck le (hun′ē suk′l), any of a group of shrubs or vines, some with small flowers.

Hong Kong (hong′kong′), a British colony adjoining southeast China.

-hood (*suffix*), a group of.

hos tile (hos′tl), unfriendly; unfavorable.

hus tle (hus′l), *Informal.* tireless energy.

Hy dra (hī′drə), a Greek mythological serpent having nine heads.

i

-ial (*suffix*), form of **-al.**

-ian (*suffix*), form of **-an.**

-ible (*suffix*), form of **-able.**

-ic (*suffix*), having to do with.

i den ti cal (ī den′tə kl), exactly alike.

i den ti fy (ī den′tə fī), to recognize as being a certain person or thing.

ig nore (ig nôr′), to pay no attention to.

im- (*prefix*), form of **in-,** ·used before *b, m, p.*

im age (im′ij), a likeness; description or figure of speech which helps the mind form pictures.

im i tate (im′ə tāt), to copy.

in- (*prefix*), not; the opposite of.

in ci dent (in′sə dənt), an event.

in crease (in krēs′), to become greater.

In di a (in′dē ə), a country in south Asia.

in di cate (in′də kāt), to point out; show.

in dig nant (in dig′nənt), angry at a mean or unjust action.

in dus try (in′dəs trē), any branch of trade, business, or manufacture; effort; hard work.

in hab i tant (in hab′ə tənt), one who lives in a certain place.

ini tial (i nish′əl), the first.

in or di nate (in ôrd′n it), excessive.

in so lence (in′sə ləns), bold impoliteness; insulting speech or action.

in tel lect (in′tə lekt), a great mental ability.

in tel li gent (in tel′ə jənt), quick at learning.

in tense (in tens′), very great.

inter- (*prefix*), between.

in tone (in tōn′), to chant; to read or speak in a singing voice.

in ves ti gate (in ves′tə gāt), to examine carefully and thoroughly by observation, inquiry, and study of facts.

in volve (in volv′), to include.

-ion (*suffix*), the act of; the state of.

ir- (*prefix*), form of **in-**.

ir ri tate (ir′ə tāt), to make angry.

-ish (*suffix*), belonging to.

-ism (*suffix*), the act of being.

-ist (*suffix*), one who knows about.

-ity (*suffix*), the state or condition of being.

-ive (*suffix*), having to do with; likely to.

i vo ry (ī′və rē), the hard, white or nearly white, bone substance forming the tusks of elephants.

-ize (*suffix*), make; become.

j

jave lin (jav′lən), a light spear.

ju bi lant (jü′bl ənt), joyful.

ju ni per (jü′nə pər), a low evergreen shrub or tree with small, dark blue berries.

jus tice (jus′tis), fairness; rightness.

l

lab o ra to ry (lab′ə rə tô′rē), a place where scientific work is done.

Lat in (lat′n), the language of the ancient Romans.

lat i tude (lat′ə tüd), the imaginary east-west lines around the earth which are used to measure and record the distance north and south of the equator.

lep re chaun (lep′rə kôn), in Irish legends, an elf who looks like a little old man, is a cobbler, and has hidden treasure.

-less (*suffix*), without; that does not; that cannot be.

li (lē), a Chinese coin of little value.

li no le um (lə nō′lē əm), a floor covering.

lob (lob), in tennis, a ball hit high to the back of the opponent's court.

log ic (loj′ik), the science of proof or reasoning.

Lon don (lun′dən), the capital of Great Britain, located in England.

loom (lüm), to appear in the distance, usually as overly large and hazy.

Lou is ville (lü′ē vil), a city in northern Kentucky.

lute (lüt), a stringed muscial instrument.

-ly (*suffix*), the manner of being; like.

lyre (lir), a stringed musical instrument of ancient times similar to a small harp.

---

hat, āge, cãre, fäther; let, ēqual, tėrm; it, ice; hot, ōpen, ôrder; oil; house; cup, fùll, rüle, ūse; th, thin; ᴛʜ, then; zh, measure; ə represents *a* in about, *e* in taken, *i* in April, *o* in lemon, *u* in circus.

m

mag nif i cent (mag nif′ə snt), richly decorated; splendid; grand.

maj es ty (maj′is tē), title used in speaking to or of a king; dignity.

Ma lay a (mə lā′ə), a member country of the Federation of Malaysia in southeast Asia.

mal let (mal′it), a wooden hammer.

Man hat tan (man hat′n), an island on which the most important business district of New York City is located.

ma rine (mə rēn′), having to do with the ocean.

mea ger (mē′gər), poor.

med i tate (med′ə tāt), to think; reflect.

Med i ter ra ne an (med′ə tə rā′nē ən), a large sea between Europe and Africa.

-ment (*suffix*), the act of; the state of.

mer chant (mer′chənt), a person who buys and sells, a storekeeper.

mere (mir), only.

mer maid (mer′mād′), an imaginary creature, half woman and half fish.

me te or ite (mē′tē ər ĭt), a stony or metallic mass that falls to the earth from outer space; a fallen meteor.

-meter (*combining form*), a device for measuring.

micro- (*combining form*), one millionth of a _____ ; very small.

mink (mingk), a small mammal, somewhat like a weasel, whose fur is valuable.

mint (mint), to coin money.

mis- (*prefix*), bad.

mod ule (moj′ùl), a self-contained structure of a spacecraft that performs particular tasks in support of the primary function of the craft.

mois ture (mois′chər), a slight wetness in the air or on a surface.

mon i tor (mon′ə tər), a student chosen to carry out special duties at school.

mon u ment (mon′yə mənt), something, such as a statue, set up in memory of an event or person.

mor tal (môr′tl), a human being.

mourn (môrn), to feel or express sorrow.

muf fle (muf′l), to deaden a sound.

mur mur (mėr′mər), a sound heard on stethoscope produced by incorrect opening and closing of heart valves.

muse (mūz), to think.

mut ter (mut′ər), to speak in low tones in a complaining manner; grumble.

myth (mith), a legend or story which usually attempts to explain some happening in nature.

myth o log i cal (mith′ə loj′ə kl), of the study of legends explaining mysteries in nature.

n

nar rate (na rāt′), to tell a story, etc.

Na tion al Ge o graph ic (jē′ ə-graf′ik), a monthly magazine containing many articles and pictures which help explain geography.

-ness (*suffix*), the state or condition of being.

New Or le ans (ôr′lē ənz), a city in Louisiana.

441

Nile Valley (nīl), the valley in Africa formed by the Nile River.

no ble (nō'bl), high and great by birth, rank, or title; good.

nov el (nov'l), of a new kind; new.

nudge (nuj), to push slightly.

nui sance (nü'sns), something or someone that is disagreeable.

nu mer ous (nü'mər əs), very many.

nuz zle (nuz'l), to rub with the nose.

nymph (nimf), any one of a group of Greek or Roman goddesses of nature.

o

of fend (ə fend'), to hurt one's feelings.

O lym pics (ō lim'piks), modern, international athletic contests held every four years.

op er ate (op'ər āt), to be at work; run; perform surgery.

op po nent (ə pō'nənt), the one on the other side, as in a contest, game, or fight.

op por tune (op'ər tün'), favorable; well-chosen.

op po site (op'ə zit), as different as can be; placed against.

-or (*suffix*), a person or thing that. See **-er.**

or gan ism (ôr'gən iz əm), a living body that has an organized structure.

or gan ize (ôr'gən īz), to arrange in working order; to bring together into a group people having a common interest.

O ri ent (ô'rē ənt), the East; countries in Asia.

or ni thol o gy (ôr'nə thol'ə jē), the study of birds.

-ous (*suffix*), having; full of.

p

Pan a ma (pan'ə mä), a Central American country on a narrow neck of land connecting North America and South America.

pan ic (pan'ik), a sudden, unreasoning fear.

par a dise (par'ə dīs), any place or state of great happiness and beauty; heaven.

par don (pärd'n), to set free from punishment; forgive.

Par is (par'is), a city in east-central Illinois; the capital and largest city of France.

par tic i pate (pär tis'ə pāt), to take part.

par ti cle (pär'tə kl), a little piece.

par ti tion (pär tish'ən), a wall between rooms.

pea cock (pē'kok'), a large bird, about the size of a turkey, with beautiful feathers of many colors.

peas ant (pez'nt), a farmer of the working class in Europe.

Pe o ri a (pē ô'rē ə), a city in west-central Illinois.

per mis sion (pər mish'ən), consent.

per plex (pər pleks'), to puzzle.

per sist ent (pər sis'tənt), willing and able to continue, especially in the face of trouble.

per suade (pər swād'), to win over, to do or believe.

phi los o phy (fə los'ə fē), the study of truth.

---

hat, āge, cãre, fäther; let, ēqual, tėrm; it, īce; hot, ōpen, ôrder; oil; house; cup, fũll, rüle, ūse; th, thin; ᴛн, then; zh, measure; ə represents *a* in about, *e* in taken, *i* in April, *o* in lemon, *u* in circus.

phoe be (fē′bē), a small, American fly-catching bird with a crested head.

phoe nix (fē′niks), a mythical bird.

pho to graph (fō′tə graf), a picture made with a camera.

plan et oid (plan′ə toid), any of several small planets between Jupiter and Mars; an asteroid.

plas tic (plas′tik), any of various substances that harden and retain their shape after being molded.

ply (plī), to work with; use.

pop u lar (pop′yə lər), well-liked.

pop u la tion (pop′yə lā′shən), the total number of people.

por tage (pôr′tij), to carry boats and supplies across land.

post- (*prefix*), after.

po ten tial (pə ten′shəl), the ability to become.

prac ti cal (prak′tə kl), useful.

prac ti cal ly (prak′tik lē), almost.

pre cise (pri sīs′), exact.

pre dic a ment (pri dik′ə mənt), a difficult or dangerous situation.

pre fer (pri fėr′), to like better.

prej u dice (prej′ə dis), an opinion formed without taking time to make a fair judgment.

pres sure (presh′ər), weight or force.

priv i lege (priv′l ij), a special right.

pro ceed ing (prə sēd′ing), an action in a case in a court of law.

pro fes sion (prə fesh′ən), a specific kind of work that requires special education.

prof it (prof′it), to receive good; benefit.

pro logue (prō′lôg), a speech addressed to the audience by an actor at the beginning of a play.

prompt (prompt), on time; quick; done without delay.

prop er ty (prop′ər tē), the furniture and other things (except scenery and clothes) used by the actors in a play; thing or things owned; **chemical property,** a specific quality or power belonging to something.

pros e cute (pros′ə kūt), to bring before a court of law.

pro vi sions (prə vizh′əns), supplies.

psy chol o gy (sī kol′ə jē), the science of the mind.

pub lish (pub′lish), to prepare and offer something such as a book, music, etc., for sale.

pum mel (pum′l), to beat with the fists.

pur loin (pėr loin′), to steal.

q

qual i fy (kwol′ə fī), to show oneself fit for something, as for a job.

qual i ty (kwol′ə tē), something special about an object that makes it what it is.

quan ti ty (kwon′tə tē), a certain amount.

quar an tine (kwôr′ən tēn), the state of being kept away from others for a specific time period in order to prevent the spreading of infectious diseases.

qua ver (kwā′vər), to shake.

quest (kwest), to search; hunt.

quiv er (kwiv′ər), to shake; tremble.

quo ta tion (kwō tā′shən), the stating of the current price of a stock or bond.

r

ra di um (rā′dē əm), a radioactive metallic element found in uranium ores.

re- (*prefix*), again; back.

re cede (ri sēd′), to move backward.

rec om mend (rek′ə mend′), to speak in favor of.

re gion (rē′jən), any large part of the earth's surface; area.

ren dez vous (rän′də vü), a meeting place; an agreement to meet at a certain place and time.

rep u ta tion (rep′yə tā′shən), the character of a person as seen or judged by others.

re quest (ri kwest′), to ask for as a favor; what is asked for.

re quire (ri kwīr′), to have need for.

re sist (ri zist′), to fight against.

res o lute (rez′ə lüt), firm; bold.

re spon si ble (ri spon′sə bl), deserving credit.

rheu mat ic (rü mat′ik), having swelling and stiffness of the joints.

ro tate (rō′tāt), to turn in a circle.

rub ble (rub′l), broken pieces of stone, brick, etc.

ruf fle (ruf′l), unevenness.

rum ple (rum′pl), to wrinkle; muss up.

s

sage (sāj), a very wise man.

Sag it tar i us (saj′ə tär′ē əs), a southern constellation of stars.

sanc tu ar y (sangk′chù er′ē), a place where one feels safe and peaceful.

sap ling (sap′ling), a young tree.

saun ter (sôn′tər), to walk along slowly and happily.

scar let (skär′lit), a very bright red.

scarp (skärp), a steep slope.

scene (sēn), a particular happening in a play.

sched ule (skej′ùl), a timetable.

schol ar (skol′ər), a person having much knowledge.

scour (skour), to clean.

scrab ble (skrab′l), to scramble; claw at.

scrag gly (skrag′lē), rough; jagged.

scruff (skruf), the skin at the back of the neck.

sculp tor (skulp′tər), one who carves works of art out of stone, marble, metal.

scur ry (skėr′ē), to hurry.

se cure (si kyùr′), certain; free from danger.

seis mic de tec tor (sīz′mik di tek′tər), an instrument that automatically detects and records the great force, direction, and time period of any ground movement or quake; a seismograph.

ser en dip i ty (ser′ən dip′ə tē), the ability to make lucky and unexpected discoveries by accident.

se ri al num ber (sir′ē əl), a special number given to an article, or a person.

serv ice (sėr′vis), in tennis, the act of putting the ball into play.

sham ba (sham′bə), an African plantation.

sheath (shēth), a carrying case for a knife.

shot-put (shot′ pùt), a contest in which one throws a heavy metal ball as far as he can.

shriv el (shriv′l), to wrinkle and draw up.

sig na ture (sig′nə chər), a person's name written by himself.

---

hat, āge, cãre, fäther; let, ēqual, tėrm; it, īce; hot, ōpen, ôrder; oil; house; cup, fùll, rüle, ūse; th, thin; ᴛʜ, then; zh, measure; ə represents *a* in about, *e* in taken, *i* in April, *o* in lemon, *u* in circus.

sin ew (sin′ū), a tough, fibrous tissue that joins muscle to bone; tendon.

sis al (sis′l), a cactuslike plant that yields a white fiber that is used to make rope.

sit u ate (sich′ủ āt), to place; locate.

sit u a tion (sich′ủ ā′shən), a circumstance; condition.

sky lark (skī′lärk′), to play merrily; frolic.

slab (slab), a broad, thick, flat piece.

slack (slak), to let up on; lessen.

slump (slump), to drop heavily and suddenly.

so ber (sō′bər), serious.

so di um chlo ride (sō′dē əm klô′rĭd), common table salt.

sol i tude (sol′ ə tüd), being alone.

so lu tion (sə lü′shən), the solving of a problem; answer.

soothe (süтн), to calm; comfort.

source (sôrs), the place from which anything comes.

spewn (spūn), thrown out.

Sphinx (sfingks), a creature from Greek and Roman mythology.

sta di um (stā′dē əm), a large place for outdoor games, having rows of seats around an open space.

stam mer (stam′ ər), to hesitate in speech; stutter.

-stat (*combining form*), brought to a stand; fixed.

stealthy (stel′thē), done in a secret manner; sly.

stern (stėrn), grim; firm.

St. Louis (sānt lü′is), a city in Missouri, on the Mississippi River.

stock (stok), a supply of.

strat e gy (strat′ə jē), the skillful planning and management of anything.

sub side (səb sīd′), to die down.

sub sti tute (sub′stə tüt), a thing that is used instead of another.

sub way (sub′wā′), an electric railroad running beneath the streets of a city.

suc ceed (sək sēd′), to do well.

sul phur (sul′fər), a yellow nonmetallic chemical element.

sum mon (sum′ ən), to order to come; arouse.

sup er vise (sü′pər vīz), to keep check on and direct activities.

surge (sėrj), a movement forward by great force.

sur geon (sėr′jən), a doctor who is trained and licensed to perform operations.

sur plus (sėr′pləs), something left over; excess.

t

tax i der my (tak′sə dėr′mē), the art of preparing, stuffing, and mounting animals in lifelike form.

tech nol o gy (tek nol′ə jē), the applying of industrial and scientific skills to practical uses.

-teen (*suffix*), ten.

tele- (*word element*), far; over a distance.

tempt (tempt), to try to persuade a person to do something.

ter ror (ter′ər), a great fear.

Thebes (thēbz), an important city in ancient Greece.

theft (theft), an act of stealing; robbery.

the o ry (thē′ə rē), an explanation based on reasoning.

thermo- (*combining form*), heat.

thick et (thik′it), a thick growth of shrubs, bushes, or small trees.

Ti bet (ti bet′), a section of China located on a high plateau in the southwestern part.

-tion (*suffix*), the act of; the state of.

445

tor pe do (tôr pē′dō), a large, cigar-shaped, explosive shell that travels under water and is used in warfare to destroy enemy ships.

tour na ment (tėr′nə mənt), a contest involving many persons for a championship in some sport.

tra di tion (trə dish′ən), the handing down from parents to children such things as beliefs and customs.

Tran quil i ty Base (trang kwil′ə tē), the tiny moon patch that was named by Mr. Armstrong and Col. Aldrin, Jr., who inhabited this desolate plain for 21½ hours.

trans- (*prefix*), across.

trans late (trans lāt′), to change from one language to another.

treach er y (trech′ər ē), a breaking of faith while pretending to be loyal.

tres- (*prefix*), a form of **trans-**

trick le (trik′l), to flow slowly in drops or in a small stream.

tri um phant (trĭ um′fənt), rejoicing because of victory or success.

tu mult (tü′mult), a noisy uproar or disorder.

Tus cum bi a (tus kum′bi ē), a town in northwestern Alabama.

tus sle (tus′l), to struggle.

-ty (*suffix*), tens; the state or condition of being.

ty coon (tĭ kün′), a businessman with great influence and wealth; usually a leader in a certain field.

u

ul ti mate (ul′tə mit), greatest possible; final.

un- (*prefix*), not; the opposite of.

uni- (*word element*), one.

u ni corn (ū′nə kôrn), a legendary horse-like animal with a single long horn in the middle of its forehead.

u nique (ū nēk′), having no like or equal; being the only one of its kind.

u ni ver si ty (ū′nə vėr′sə tē), a school where people go for further study after high school.

up hol ster y (up hōl′stər ē), the covering for furniture.

-ure (*suffix*), the act of; the fact of.

v

vac u um tube (vak′yu̇ əm), a small, sealed glass or metal container from which almost all air has been removed to allow the passage of electric discharges between metallic shields projecting into the container from the outside.

var i ous (vãr′ē əs), several; different.

var y (vãr′ē), to alter; change.

ve loc i ty (və los′ə tē), the speed at which a thing is moving.

vic tim (vik′təm), someone or something injured or destroyed.

vi o lent (vī′ə lənt), acting with strong, rough force.

vis i ble (viz′ə bl), can be seen.

vol ley (vol′ē), the hitting back and forth of a tennis ball.

---

hat, āge, cãre, fäther; let, ēqual, tėrm; it, īce; hot, ōpen, ôrder; oil; house; cup, fu̇ll, rüle, ūse; th, thin; ŦH, then; zh, measure; ə represents *a* in about, *e* in taken, *i* in April, *o* in lemon, *u* in circus.

vul can ize (vul′kən īz), to treat rubber with sulfur and heat to make it more elastic and durable.

W

waive (wāv), to put aside (as a requirement); excuse.

-ward (*suffix*), in the direction of; toward.

wa ver (wā′vər), to become unsteady; begin to give way.

whim per (hwim′pər), to cry with low, broken sounds.

wield (wēld), to hold and use.

wince (wins), to draw back quickly from something.

wit (wit), mind; understanding.

with er (wiŦH′ər), to dry up; to lose freshness.

wit ness (wit′nis), a person who saw something happen.

wrath (rath), a very great anger; rage.

wres tle (res′l), to struggle.

wretch ed (rech′id), very unhappy; miserable.

writhe (rīŦH), to twist and turn; be very uncomfortable.

wry (rī), twisted; a facial expression showing disgust.

X

X ray (eks′rā′), a ray that has a short wave length which is used to photograph solids such as bones or organs within the human body.

Y

-y (*suffix*), resembling; full of.

yore (yôr), of long ago; in the past.

Z

ze bra (zē′brə), a wild, horselike mammal, striped with dark bands on white.

zest (zest), a keen enjoyment; vigor.

B. Characters

Ake ley (āk′li)
An Li (än lē′)
Au du bon (ô′də bon)
Baeke land (bāk′land)
Bar rett (bar′ət)
Beat ty (bē′tē)
Coch ran (kok′rən)
Critch ley (krich′li)
Crook ham (krŭk′həm)
Cu rie (kyùr′ē or kyù re′)
Did rik son (dēd′rik sən)
Din wid die (din′wid ē)
Ec rette (āk ret′)
Fran çois (fräN′swä′)
Gag non (gag noN′)
Gros ve nor (grōv′nèr)
Han wu-ti (hän′wü tē′)
Hor ace (hôr′is)
Le o nore (le′ə nôr)
Lin Foo (lēng′fü′)
Mad a gas car (mad′ə gas′kər)

Mal vi na (mal vē′nə)
Mar i et ta (mär′i et′ə)
Mat thew (math′ū)
Me loche (mə lôsh′)
Mi chel (mē′shel′)
Mi das (mī′dəs)
Nes sel rode (nes′əl rōd)
Nich o las (nik′l əs)
Noo man (nü′mən)
Oed i pus (ed′ə pəs)
Pe pe (pe′pe)
Ponce de Le ón (pons′də lē′ən)
Ri ta (rē′tə)
Ru fus (rü′fəs)
Syl vain (sil vaN′)
The o dore (thē′ə dôr′)
Thwick le (thwik′əl)
Tung-fang Su (tung′fäng sü′)
Va ran gi (və ran′jē)
von Roent gen (von rent′gən)
Wing Soong (wing süng′)

ILLUSTRATORS:

Ed Augustiny	Bart Jerner	Rick Schreiter
Muriel and Jim Collins	Herb Kane	Amos Sewell
David Cunningham	Carl Kock	Bill Shires
James Curran	Robert Kresin	George Suyeoka
John Everds	H. Charles McBarron	Thornton Utz
Larry Frederick	Tak Murakami	Jan Wills
John Henry	Jerry Pinkney	

87654321

7172737475